DATE DUE

GAYLORD   #3523PI   Printed in USA

JASON!

Jason!

by

Colston West

EAGLE HOUSE
PRESS

Copyright © 2005 Leonard Colston West

First published in 2005 by Eagle House Press
43 Eagle Road
Brislington
Bristol BS4 3LQ

Distributed by Gazelle Book Services Limited
Hightown, White Cross Mills, South Rd, Lancaster, England LA1 4XS

British Library Cataloguing in Publication Data
A catalogue record for this book is available from the British Library

ISBN 0-9547338-0-0

Typeset by Amolibros, Milverton, Somerset
This book production has been managed by Amolibros
Printed and bound by T J International Ltd, Padstow, Cornwall, UK

Preface

This book was prompted by my grand-daughters who asked some time ago if I could recommend a story about Jason and the Argonauts which was easy to read. I said I would look and report back.

After much searching, I failed to find a book which I thought they would like. So I decided that I would help Jason to write his story. It is interesting that his account agrees in the main with numerous but sometimes fragmentary ancient sources (mainly Pindar and Apollodorus) for his schooldays, with Apollonius's *Argonautica* for the journey of the Argo and with Ovid's *Metamorphoses* for part of what happened afterwards.

Jason speaks for himself, and how he did this you will discover in due course. I have tried to make his journey easier to understand by converting his ancient bronze-age units of measurement (Jason was a fanatic about numeracy and measurements) into modern (but non-metric) equivalents.

At the end of his story I have helped by providing a glossary which contains an annotated list of the names of the original fifty-five Argonauts in alphabetical order.

The book is divided into sixty-one short chapters, suitable for bed-time reading to and by children aged 10 to 100.

C W

Contents

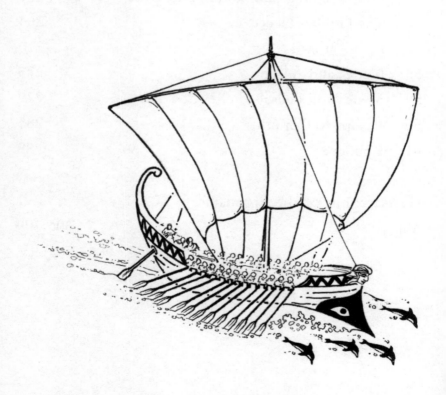

1

How it all started

I first met Peleus on the sixth day before my fourteenth birthday. I was down on my farm, freshening up after a hard afternoon's work with my sheep and cattle. I had sent my farm steward and our two farm labourers home, and was washing my hands in the water-trough when I was propelled headfirst into the trough itself by some irresistible force from behind me.

"Oops!" said a gruff voice as my head emerged from the water. "Oops, oh dear, I am so terribly sorry," continued the voice. "Please let me help you out. Here, take my hand!" I held out my hand, and the owner of the gruff voice pulled me out of the trough. When I had cleared the water from my eyes, there was this stranger, dusty from much travel, dressed in a sheepskin cloak over a simple linen tunic.

"I must have tripped over that tree-root there," said the voice. "My name is Peleus. What's yours?" he continued.

"I'm Jason," I replied. "Peleus...er...haven't I heard of you?"

"Most people have," he replied. "My father's name is Aeacus and my mother's is Endeis, and she is the daughter of the Centaur Cheiron who, I understand, is the headmaster of a school somewhere near here. In fact it's my mother, Endeis, whom I'm trying to find. I've been told she teaches at my grandfather's school, and since I'm lost, I'd be grateful for any help you can give me on the whereabouts of the school. It's called 'Cheiron's School for Heroes'."

"I most certainly can," I replied. "I'm one of the pupils of that school, and have been for as long as I can remember. Of course I know your mother. She's one of my teachers and your grandfather is my headmaster."

"Well I'll be blowed," replied Peleus. "There's a stroke of luck, falling into you like that. I'm sorry, I didn't mean that literally. I'm not normally so accident prone. I say, you are rather wet, you know."

"Think nothing of it," I replied, somewhat unconvincingly.

So I explained who I was, what I was doing on the school farm, and said I would gladly show him the way to Cheiron's School for Heroes.

"Perhaps you could fill me in about your strange school before you show me the way there. To be quite honest, I could do with a short rest, in spite of being a bit hungry."

"I do apologise," I replied. "I'm forgetting my duty as your host. I've some good cold beef in the farmhouse. I'll get some for you and we can sit on that bench over there in the shade of the oak tree, have a bite to eat and I'll tell you all about Cheiron's School for Heroes."

"What are the buildings like?" asked Peleus, when we had settled ourselves under the oak tree.

"Well," I said, "Cheiron's School for Heroes is not like any school you are likely to know. For a start, there are no buildings—only a series of well-concealed caves set into the mountain-side. For security reasons, there is only one main entrance, which can be effectively sealed by rolling a large but round and smooth boulder across the entrance. There are, of course, other small emergency exits to the right and left of the main entrance, but these are very small and kept blocked from the inside. The caverns inside are quite spacious. There are three of these: the main one at the front where most of the teaching takes place, the second a large dormitory for the students and the third where meals are cooked and eaten, and that one has a natural funnel in the roof which normally takes most of the smoke from the cooking away. There are other smaller caverns which serve as bedrooms for the teaching and domestic staff. Small trees and shrubs grow all along the cave entrances, which have the effect of camouflaging the whole school. Not that there is normally any danger from outsiders, but, as Cheiron often says, 'You never know!' "

"What about this strange headmaster of yours?" asked Peleus. "I've heard he has four legs!"

"That sounds rather rude," I replied. "You had better mind your words when you are talking within his earshot. He can be rather touchy."

"I'll certainly bear that in mind," said Peleus.

"Cheiron, my headmaster," I continued, "I suppose, is a kind of 'wizard'. Let me explain. He is a centaur, that is to say, part horse and part man. Centaurs as whole have a very bad reputation. They are descended from Ixion, a Thessalian king who was thoroughly bad and was punished accordingly. His son, by name Centaurus, mated with Magnesian mares on the slopes of Mount Pelion, and their offspring were the monstrous centaurs. They suffer from their origins and tend to be brutal and fierce. They continue to live in the forests growing on the northern reaches of Mount Pelion, but keep their distance from Cheiron and his School for Heroes. Cheiron, however, though physically a centaur, had very different origins."

"I suppose you are going to describe them to me in some detail," interrupted Peleus.

"Yes," I replied.

"I thought you might," said Peleus.

"Well," I continued, "Cronos, son of Uranus, during the time when he reigned over the Titans (primeval gods, you know) and Zeus was still being nurtured in a Cretan cave, deceived his jealous consort Rhea and went to bed with Philyra, a daughter of Ocean (another Titan). It all went wrong. Rhea caught them in the act. Cronos leapt up, trying to disguise himself by turning himself into a stallion with a flowing mane. He made off, but not before Philyra had become pregnant. She decided to leave the island where she lived in shame and made her home on the flanks of Mount Pelion's ridges. Nine months later she gave birth to Cheiron. From the waist up he had the body of a man, but from his waist downwards (and backwards!) he was a magnificent stallion, with four legs and hooves. As a result, he has the dexterous skills of a human combined with the speed of a horse, which is useful for getting out of dangerous situations. He is, of course, very different from the wild centaurs who were descended from Ixion."

"Of course," muttered Peleus.

"For a start," I went on, "he is kind and friendly. He is also extremely wise: his skills include medicine [useful where

4

doctors were few and far between], archery and hunting [useful for self-preservation]. Rumour has it that he did at some time receive instruction in the art of prophecy from no less than the gods Apollo and Artemis; if this is true, he keeps very quiet about it and he certainly does not include prophecy in the school syllabus, at least not as long as I have been a pupil. However, he loves music and makes sure it is included as a main-stream subject at all levels, and not just an 'extra'. And to cap it all, Cheiron was born an immortal, which is not surprising if you remember his parentage."

Peleus yawned.

"If you are tired," I asked, considerately, "would you like to sleep here the night, and carry on to the school tomorrow?"

"No, no, no," he replied. "It's just the fresh air here. But tell me, I know my mother teaches at the school, but what about the other staff?"

"Well," I said, "there are three other members of staff besides Cheiron, namely: Cheiron's mother, his wife and his daughter, who is your mother, of course!

"First there is *Philyra*, his mother. At first she took a long time getting used to the unusual shape of her son; she succeeded in the end, came to live with him in his school and took charge of the nursery department and the kindergarten. I came to know and love her as I progressed through the school. She taught me all kinds of domestic subjects including cooking, sewing and domestic hygiene, all of which may possibly come in very useful one day. Philyra must have been quite old when I joined the school; I suspect that she too is immortal.

"Secondly, there is Cheiron's wife, *Chariclo*, who does most of the academic teaching. To be quite honest, Cheiron is more at ease with the practical rather than the academic side of things. He is never happier than when he is teaching hunting and fighting and self-defence, and he is very good at these. He believes that boys should be brought up to be tough and self-reliant, and that is where he fails with me, because I like working with others, particularly on the farm. Chariclo has learnt a lot from Cheiron, and she enjoys teaching us in the mornings, while Cheiron is out hunting on his own—he loves racing around the forests of the Pelion ridge without the encumbrance of students. In the afternoons, Cheiron takes over the outdoor activities while Chariclo enjoys her hobbies which include needlework and making medicines from plants and herbs, as well as supervising the few domestic staff who prepare the main meal of the day which we all share together at the end of the day.

"And thirdly, there is his daughter, *Endeis*, who is your mother, of course.

"Of course," said Peleus.

I was beginning to get the impression that Peleus was not, perhaps, interested in too much detail, but I decided not to hold that against him.

"Cheiron," I continued, "had two other daughters, Hippo and Ocyrrhoe, but they had left home before my time at the school. They would be your aunts, of course."

Peleus nodded in agreement. "Let me explain something briefly," he said. " Endeis married a very pious man called Aeacus (my father of course), who still lives on the island of Aegina, way down south near Athens. Endeis left Aeacus, who got angry after a very unfortunate incident when I accidentally killed my stepbrother. She came back to help her mother with the teaching at your school."

"That's very interesting," I said, "and an excellent teacher she is too."

"Good of you to say so," said Peleus. "But I'll tell you more of my family history later."

"I'll look forward to that," I said.

Then, strangely enough, neither of us spoke for a while as we finished eating our snack. Then Peleus said, "Right then, if you are dry enough, let's be on our way. I'm looking forward to seeing my mother again, and I expect you are keen to get back to school after a hard day's work on your farm."

"My farm work is part of my schooling," I said. "But I'll tell you all about that later on."

"I expect you will," said Peleus, as we gathered up our gear and set off along the hillside.

2

We arrive at the School for Heroes

"How far is it?" asked Peleus. "I hope it's not far, because my feet have just about had it for today."

"The last time I paced it," I replied, "it was 4,620 feet, but that's only approximate. My measurement methods are rather primitive, I'm afraid."

Peleus looked at me rather strangely. "You mean it's only about a mile," he said after a while. "I think I can manage that."

Peleus seemed a pleasant sort of chap, and as we toiled up the side of the mountain, we chatted amiably. My clothes were nearly dry by the time we arrived at the school.

As we turned round the last clump of trees on the path leading up to the school, it so happened that we ran into Endeis, Peleus's mother, who was out for her customary evening stroll before joining us for dinner. Endeis and Peleus greeted each other with hugs, and when they stood apart Endeis exclaimed:

"Lovely to see you after all this time. But what have you been doing, you young rascal? How did you get that blood all over your forehead? You haven't been fighting again, have you? And with Jason, too, when you've only known him for five minutes."

"Oh, Mother," he said, "you do jump to conclusions, don't you? I simply knocked my head on a low branch of an oak tree as we climbed up the hill."

It was true; Peleus had in fact knocked his head several times coming up the hill, in spite of my warnings of low branches.

"Now tell me," continued Endeis, "what have you and your brother Telamon been up to since we all had to leave Aegina? I presume your father Aeacus is still king there. Is he still mad at us about the death of your poor half-brother Phocus? Have you made any more attempts to try to get it into his thick skull how it was all a very silly accident?"

(Aegina, incidentally, is an island in the Saronic Gulf,

about twenty miles to the south-west of Athens, and about a hundred miles, as the crow flies, from the school.)

"Afraid not, Mother dear," replied Peleus. "But Telamon had a go at explaining it all to Father, who actually allowed him to approach the shore of Aegina in a boat, and shout his explanations from the deck. But it didn't work. So Telamon went back to Salamis, where I understand that he is well in with King Cychreus, and is minded to marry his daughter Glauce."

(Salamis, incidentally, is another island in the Saronic Gulf, north of Aegina and due west of Athens. I learnt all this from Endeis's geography lessons when I was in the junior school.)

"Well done old Telamon!" said Endeis. "And what have you been doing meanwhile?"

"Well, I went further than Telamon, and ended up in Phthia, which as you know is where Eurytion purified me from my apparent crime in killing Phocus. He let me marry his daughter Antigone and gave me a third of his country. However, for some reason or other, I seem to have fallen out of favour there, for a while at least. So I decided to come here to see how you were getting on."

There was a rather icy silence in the conversation at this point. Eventually Endeis said, "Are you sure that was the reason you came here? Come on, be honest!"

Peleus blushed. In all the time I knew him, this was one of the few times I observed him to be seriously embarrassed.

"Well, to be quite honest," Peleus stammered, "I had a dream. I dreamt that Hermes came and stood over me and told me to come here, and ask Cheiron for further instructions."

I expected Endeis to say something like "A likely story!" or "What was the real reason you left Phthia?", but all she said was, "So that was it, was it? Well, that makes sense."

Peleus looked puzzled, but Endeis had assumed the distant expression that so often comes over those who seem able to look into the future. Her father, Cheiron, also could often be seen staring curiously into the distance.

All this interested me intensely. So, after what I thought was a decent interval, I asked Peleus whether he could describe how Phocus had met his accident.

Peleus, surprisingly, seemed very willing to fill me in with the background details.

"Well, if you must know, Jason, it was like this. My father Aeacus was a bit of a lad, and had also fathered Phocus by a Nereid called Psamathe. Nereids, if you didn't know," (I did), "are daughters of Nereus, the ancient sea-god, and have the power of metamorphosis. So Psamathe changed herself into a seal to try to escape the attentions of Aeacus. She did not succeed, and in due course produced Phocus, who grew up to be very handsome and athletic.

"One day, we were all exercising together on the playing field behind the palace, when brother Telamon was showing off throwing the discus. I was running past him when I stumbled and, as bad luck would have it, I jerked his arm. The discus went wildly off course, and struck Phocus on the head, killing him outright. Endeis had been watching us, and saw what had happened. She was very worried because she thought that Aeacus would not believe it was an accident, since it was well known that Endeis, Telamon and I were somewhat jealous of Phocus, who was the apple of his father's eye. So we did the most stupid thing imaginable—we carried off the body of Phocus and buried it in a wood. Unfortunately we were seen, Aeacus found the body, blamed all three of us, and expelled us from Aegina forthwith. Endeis came here, Telamon went to Salamis and I went to Phthia. End of story."

"So it was all an accident, after all," I commented.

"Of course it was," replied Peleus. "Well, I tell you, I am not normally accident-prone, but that particular accident certainly had serious repercussions."

Endeis had been listening to all this very patiently.

"It's time you both had a wash before you sit down for dinner," she said. "Really, Peleus, you look as though you haven't washed since last I saw you. And as for you, young Jason, you look as though you've been pulled through a hedge backwards; either that, or fallen in a cattle-trough."

As we started towards school, Cheiron came trotting into the playground. He had a brace of hares hung round his neck and was obviously in a very good mood.

"Hello there, young Peleus," he cried. "And about time too! I see you met up with young Jason. Good! Good! Very good! You can learn a lot from each other, I am sure. Now then, we must have dinner now, and then a good night's sleep. I want you both fresh for a task I have in mind for you tomorrow. Nothing difficult, I assure you. But it will be a long day for both of you. Yes, I'm glad you got here on time, Peleus. I hate lateness, and there's not much time left. In we go to dinner, then. Look sharp, there!"

As Cheiron led the way towards the school entrance, Peleus turned to me with raised eyebrows.

"What was all that about? How did he know I was coming? What did he mean about me being on time?"

I shrugged my shoulders. "I haven't the foggiest idea," I said. "Honest!"

3

I tell Peleus my life-story

My name is Jason. You may have heard of me in titles such as *Jason and the Argonauts* or *Jason and the Golden Fleece*. Maybe you have read books or watched films with such titles. If so, you simply do not know my whole story. I was born over three thousand years ago (it is impossible for me to be precise), but it so happens that I have at last been given this opportunity to give you a first-hand account of my school days and subsequent adventures. How I am able to do so will be revealed as my tale unfolds.

Perhaps I should explain that Cheiron's School for Heroes was situated high up on the western slopes of a long mountain ridge, several miles inland from the eastern shore of the Gulf of Pagasae, and about twelve miles away southeast from the city of Iolcos.

Where is Iolcos? When I was born, it was a small but thriving city on the coast of Thessaly in ancient Greece. Today, so I am told, it is called Vólos and is the third largest port in Greece.

If you care to consult a map of northern Greece, you will see that Vólos stands on the eastern side of the central Greek mainland, in a district of Thessaly called Magnesia, at the northern end of the gulf of Pagasae. This Gulf is formed by a long claw-like promontory, which curves east and then south from the mainland, and then turns its tip westwards again, leaving a small but safe entrance to the Gulf. Down this claw-like promontory lies the long undulating ridge of Mount Pelion, with its highest point (over 5,000 feet above sea-level) at its northern end, and, as I have already said, my school was situated high up on the western slopes of this ridge.

Peleus's arrival at dinner caused quite a stir among my schoolmates. Cheiron told me that I was to be responsible for introducing Peleus to the school's rules and regulations. I was told that I could move into the spare small dormitory with him, since, said Cheiron, it was unlikely that I would be able to resist the temptation to tell Peleus all about myself well into the small hours of the night.

I was puzzled by this since it was obvious that I was very tired. I suppose Cheiron meant that Peleus would be eager to know my history, and so it proved.

I made up two comfortable beds for us, and, when we had settled down, I asked Peleus if he would like to hear why I was a pupil of the school and a brief outline of the school's routine.

"Do I have a choice?" he asked. "You must be very tired after a day's work at the farm. Tomorrow will be soon enough, really."

"Honestly, it's no trouble," I replied. "It's quite an exciting story. You see I was born in my father's palace, four miles distant from the city of Iolcos, and I was secretly and unceremoniously bundled out of it within a few hours of my birth, and brought here.

"Of course I remember nothing of that sixteen-mile journey. According to Cheiron, who told me about it much later, the journey started at dusk and took nearly all night. The horse from whose saddle I was suspended in a bundle of purple blankets was led by a faithful servant from my parents' palace. A wet-nurse (who was to stay at the school to nurse me through babyhood) steadied the bundle as she rode on the horse. The night was dark and cold, and the track from my parents' palace to the school was rough and with several difficult streams to cross. I can think of a more comfortable way to start one's life, but it was better than the alternative."

"What was that, then?" asked Peleus, with his eyes closed.

"The alternative was to have been slaughtered by Pelias. This Pelias was the king of Iolcos (you may have heard of him), elderly but strong, cruel and ambitious. His right to the throne was suspect, and many say that my father Aeson, who was Pelias's half-brother, was the rightful heir to the throne when my grandfather, king Cretheus, died. Pelias had many supporters.

"So had my father; he had two brothers who were kings in their own right of other Greek cities, and who were prepared to support him. But the Pelias party was the stronger, and could do almost whatever it wanted. Both Aeson and Pelias had the same mother, Tyro. Aeson's father was the former king Cretheus, but Pelias's father is reputed to have been Poseidon himself, the god of the sea, and I suppose that gave him some edge over Aeson. There was a rumour that my father, for some reason or other, agreed to stand down as king until his first son (who turned out to be me) should come of age.

14

"Fortunately Pelias allowed my father and Alcimede, my mother, to live in their own separate palace, on a hill above a small township four miles to the west of Iolcos, together with their own faithful palace servants, bodyguards and supporters.

"Unfortunately Pelias had been warned by an oracle that he would one day be killed by a descendant of Aeolus, the father of king Cretheus, my grandfather. So Pelias set about arranging the murder of every prominent descendant of Aeolus that he dared to, without risking a civil war. However, he spared my father Aeson, partly because of their mother, Tyro, and partly because my father's supporters presented a potential problem.

"My mother's pregnancy in Aeson's palace was kept very secret, and when I was born, there was considerable discussion in the palace concerning my future safety. It would be twenty years before I came of age and could claim my right to the throne, and twenty years was plenty of time in which Pelias could arrange a suitable accident for me. And so it was agreed in some haste that my birth would remain a secret, and that I should be nursed and educated here, at Cheiron's School for Heroes.

"I've been here ever since then, nearly fourteen years. Perhaps I should explain that farming became quite a passion with me. To begin with, from the age of eight years, it was just another subject. Cheiron was very friendly with the local farmers, who were only too glad to have pupils from Cheiron's school to help out with the crops and the farm animals.

"The timetable is arranged so that the mornings are spent in the school-room learning academic subjects such as Music,

Mythology and Medicine (the three 'M's) as well as Reckoning, Reasoning and Recitation (the three 'R's). Then after a midday snack, the afternoons are spent out-of-doors learning Foraging (hunting for food) or Fighting or Farming (the three 'F's). Cheiron likes teaching foraging best; he loves trotting around with a brace of hares hanging round his neck. The only snag with his lessons are that it is very difficult to keep up with him, because he can show a good turn of speed with his four hunter's legs, though we have all learnt to run very fast as a result.

"But I got on with farming best of all, you know, and now Cheiron allows me to run my own farm, with my own land and farm-buildings and a good herd of cattle and sheep.

"Would you like to have an outline of the day's routine, or can that wait till morning? I must confess I am rather tired."

There was no reply. I decided I would have to ask Peleus in the morning what he had missed from my account, so that I could go over it again. However, I discovered to my consternation that Peleus snored rather loudly. So I had to stuff some lamb's wool in my ears (I always kept some in my emergency first-aid kit) before I could get some well-earned sleep.

4

Cheiron sends us on an expedition

Next morning (the fifth day before my fourteenth birthday),
Cheiron addressed the whole school after prayers.

"Good morning, boys!"

"Good morning, Headmaster!" came the unanimous
reply.

"I have an important announcement to make," continued
Cheiron. "I want you all to welcome Peleus into the sixth
form. He is sixteen years old and very experienced in hunting
and athletics, and as you know, sixth-formers are expected
to teach their skills to the lower forms. So please pay him
due respects when you receive tuition from him. He will
also be able to give you advice on accident-prevention, a
subject which so far has been absent from our syllabuses.

"And now, off you go to your classes, but you two, Jason
and Peleus, please stay behind."

When the dining room had emptied, Cheiron gave us
our task for the day.

"Nothing too difficult," he said. "It's just that I am
running out of some ingredients for my magic medicines,
and I'm very short of a particular species of marigold which
grows only, as far as I know, on the south-eastern corner
of this Pelion peninsula, on the cliffs overlooking a bay
where, I believe, the Nereids have their favourite swimming
resort."

He drew a rough map with a stone on the floor, but I did not need it. I had been there on my own several times before, during school holidays, though without Cheiron (as far as I knew) being aware of that.

"So I'd like you two to go there and pick a bag-full of marigolds for me. If you want to stay on this evening to see if you can spot the Nereids by moonlight, you can travel back through the night and sleep it off tomorrow instead of lessons. I'll tell your steward to look after the farm for you, Jason. And you, Peleus, can see something of the Pelion peninsula, and perhaps get a glimpse of the Nereid Psamathe who was poor Phocus's mother. But mind you keep out of sight!"

I packed a shoulder-bag with a day's ration of food for both of us, my first-aid kit, a rope (since we were going near cliffs) and another shoulder-bag in which to collect the marigolds.

"You believe in being prepared, don't you?" said Peleus. "In all my travels so far, I've never carried anything apart from a stout stick to ward off wild animals—and wild men, come to think of it. I live off the land—fruit, berries, nuts and spring-water."

"You mean to say you won't enjoy a nice piece of cold beef tonight for supper?" I asked him.

"You're quite right," replied Peleus. "As long as you carry the bag."

"You can carry the marigolds back," I said. "As long as they're not too heavy for you."

With which pleasantries we set off on our expedition down the peninsula. We climbed gradually up the side of the ridge as we walked southwards, skirting orchards and farms to start with, and then great forests of oak and beech as we gained height. By the early afternoon we reached the top of a saddle of the ridge from which we could see eastward across the Aegean Sea. Here we rested a while and enjoyed a light snack from the shoulder-bag—a little beef and some freshly baked bread which Philyra, Cheiron's mother, had baked the night before.

The weather was superb: an azure spring sky with wisps of cloud shielding the sun from our eyes. We rested a while after eating our snack, lying on our backs and letting the cool breeze refresh us. Then, for fun, we sparred each other with our ash staffs and found that we were fairly evenly matched. I think this pleased both of us. Cheiron had told me that Peleus was renowned as a noble and skilled fighter, and Peleus said that he had heard that all heroes trained in Cheiron's school were second to none in all Greece. So we went on our way feeling that our new friendship had got off to a good start.

By late afternoon we arrived at the south-eastern cliffs of the promontory, where we found the marigold patch, just as Peleus had told us, and as I remembered it from my previous expeditions. We collected a bag-full of the golden flowers, and then sat down for our supper.

We were overlooking a large bay that was shielded by a headland to its south. In the cliffs below us at sea level was what looked like a cave concealed by myrtle-berry bushes, and this was fronted by a wide sandy beach. The bay itself was obviously shallow; we could see the sand beneath the surface of the sea quite clearly for at least 430 feet outwards from the edge of the beach. This was the bay where I had last seen the Nereids playing and dancing to their hearts' content. If we were lucky, we would see them tonight.

The sun soon set over the hills behind us. The moon was only five days before its fullness and was beaming bright from its rising over five hours into the sky. I calculated that on my birthday in five days' time, the moon would be full and would rise as the sun was setting. All very propitious, as I pointed out to Peleus. He smiled.

"You're a remarkable fellow," he said. "I'm afraid my education has been somewhat lacking as far as numbers and reckoning and astronomy is concerned. I suppose a few years in your company and at the school will improve my deficiencies in those areas. However, for the moment, I'm happy just thinking about girls and having as good a time as possible."

"Why not indeed?" I replied. "But I think you'll find that a few years in Cheiron's School will broaden your outlook quite a bit."

"And a few years in my company," Peleus said laughing, "will broaden your outlook too, you young prig! In the meantime, where's this floor-show of Nereids I've been promised?"

"Nothing promised," I replied, "but I have a feeling we'll be lucky tonight. We just have to be patient."

And so for the next hour or so (I didn't count the minutes) we were patient. I looked forward to a good floor-show (as Peleus had called it) followed by a pleasant amble back over the ridge to an early morning breakfast.

With my new-found companion Peleus in the audience, I should have known better.

5

Peleus gets smitten

Here in the Elysian Fields, time passes in an indescribable way. Memories of those times so long ago come floating back as if they were happening now. Elysian music now fades as I remember the strains which wafted over the sea as the Nereids shimmered into the cove below us like phantoms from one of my deepest dreams.

I glanced at Peleus. He was staring down into the cove as if in a trance.

"What a wonderful sight," he said. "Fantastic! Just look how gracefully they are gliding and gyrating round the shallows there—like dolphins. And look how beautifully those on the beach are dancing. And, heavens, there's Phocus's mother Psamathe—what a smasher! No wonder Phocus had all those good looks. How many are there, Jason? There must be hundreds of them!"

"Well, I've just counted forty-nine with great difficulty—if only they would keep still for a minute or so. No, I tell a lie, there's another one just come out of the cave behind those myrtle-bushes down there. That makes the full fifty, Peleus…Peleus, come back for heaven's sake. You daren't go down there!"

"Rubbish," shouted Peleus over his shoulder as he slithered down the grass towards the cliff's edge. "That fiftieth one, I must, I simply must get to see her."

There was nothing I could do to stop him. I must say I admired the way he slithered down the cliff, using his staff to brake his speed down the steep cliff face. He ended up behind one of the myrtle-berry bushes to the side of the cave entrance. Such was his skill that his approach was almost noiseless, and the Nereids were unaware that he was there,

Thetis (for that was the name of the fiftieth Nereid) was leading the dance on the beach less than ten yards from where Peleus was hidden. Suddenly he jumped out from his hiding-place and confronted her. With a shrill shriek she and all the other Nereids turned and disappeared into the sea, and Peleus was left standing there with glazed eyes.

Eventually he turned and looked up at me. "How the hell do I get up from down here?" he shouted.

"How the hell should I know?" I replied, not without some annoyance.

"I know," he replied. "Tie one end of your rope round a tree-root, and throw the other end down here."

"Anything to oblige," I shouted back, and did as he said.

"What on earth did you think you were doing?" I asked when he was with me back on top of the cliff again.

"Did you see that girl who was leading the dance?" he replied. "What a smasher! Never in all my travels have I seen anyone so beautiful, so graceful, so…"

"Her name is Thetis," I informed him. "You seem impressed."

That glazed expression came over him again, and it was many minutes before he continued.

"I must have her. I must have her. I must. I can't help it. Jason, what can I do? How can I meet her again? How, tell me how!"

"I've no idea," I replied. "But I know someone who can tell you. If anyone can solve your problem, it's Cheiron. So let's leave it like that and get back to the school—and breakfast."

And so we set off. Peleus volunteered to carry the bag containing the heavy rope and I agreed without comment. I carried the shoulder-bag containing the marigolds.

The journey back was very pleasant for me. The moonlight made route-finding easy and the nymphs of the woods (dryads) and springs (naiads) and mountains (oreads) were easy to see as we strolled past oak-woods and over the mountain streams. As usual, I thought it was all rather magical, but Peleus was unimpressed.

"What a smasher," he kept saying, tediously. I almost pitied him, but I suspected that the events at the cove were all part of some overall plan being hatched by forces greater than I had yet encountered.

"You took your time," commented Cheiron who, surprisingly, seemed to be waiting for us when we arrived back, just as rosy-fingered dawn was appearing over the eastern hill-tops.

I handed the marigolds over to him, but he didn't seem very interested.

"What's wrong with you then, young Peleus?" he asked my glazed-looking companion.

I answered for him. "His knees had an argument with a cliff-face, and I treated them with some of your marigold ointment, sir!"

"I'm not talking about his knees," replied Cheiron, "as you very well know. Just tell me what has made him go all gooey-eyed, you young rascal!"

"He saw Thetis and hasn't recovered yet," I said.

"I'm not surprised," replied Cheiron. "I don't think he will recover, and thank you for the marigolds. If you keep slapping my ointment on his knees so liberally, you'll have to collect some more marigolds for me the next time you go over the ridge to the Nereid bay.

"And that may be sooner than you think," he added thoughtfully as he turned to go into the school for breakfast.

"What was all that about," asked Peleus, "and when can we go back to the bay to look for Thetis again?"

"I don't know and I haven't the slightest idea," I replied as we followed Cheiron into the school.

After breakfast, we were allowed to go to the dormitory to catch up with our sleep. Peleus dropped off immediately and, to judge by his snoring, was unlikely to wake until supper-time.

I slept fitfully until early afternoon. (This was the fourth day before my fourteenth birthday.) I needed some fresh air, so I crept along one of the tunnels to where a boulder blocked one of the secret entrances to the school. I carefully moved it aside sufficiently for me to squeeze through. This, of course, was strictly against school rules, but Cheiron made an exception in my case, since sometimes I had to go to and from the farm during the night, particularly during lambing.

I was still concealed by the one of the bushes which covered the secret entrance when I heard voices. Imagine my surprise when I saw Cheiron walking with a stranger. I parted the leaves of the bush to get a better view, and there, at the end of a rainbow, was a goddess I had never seen before.

6

Cheiron gets his orders

Brilliant against the dark of a passing rain cloud shone the brightest rainbow I had ever seen. It was, of course, the means by which Iris, the goddess of the rainbow and personal messenger of the goddess Hera, wife of Zeus, the supreme ruler of the gods, travelled to deliver messages from Hera, and occasionally Zeus (if Hermes happened to be busy).

"And how is Zephyrus?" Cheiron was asking Iris politely. (Zephyrus was the West Wind and was married to Iris.)

"Breezing along nicely, thank you," laughed Iris. "I must say you are looking very well, dear Cheiron."

"And what brings you here on this surprisingly rainy day?" asked Cheiron.

"Sorry about the rain," replied Iris, "but rainbows are so difficult without it, you know. Anyway, I have a message from Hera for you."

"Before you start," Cheiron said, "I think I should tell you that I already know about the trouble concerning Thetis and Zeus and Poseidon. I presume Hera has decided to settle the matter by marrying Thetis off to a mortal. Peleus, for instance. You know he's here in my school, don't you?"

Iris seemed to be somewhat amazed that Cheiron was so well informed.

"You don't miss much, do you, old Cheiron?" replied

25

Iris with a wide grin. "Of course I know that Peleus is here. Yes, it is Peleus that Thetis is to marry. You are to arrange that he wins her affections, gets engaged to her and marries her in four days' time. You are to organise the wedding and the reception afterwards. Hermes is already doing the rounds of certain gods and goddesses to invite them to the wedding. Some of them are on holiday in remote parts of the world, and Hera reckons it will need four days to ensure they get their invitations in time."

"More like a summons, if I know Hera," Cheiron commented. "And how am *I* supposed to do all that in four days, may I ask?"

"Oh, I'm so sorry," replied Iris. "Hera will supervise the Peleus's wooing of Thetis, and you can use a discreet amount of magic to prepare the wedding reception. You'll need twelve thrones for the gods and goddesses, and an almost unlimited quantity of food and wine."

"I'm glad Hera will help with the wooing, though I'm sure I can advise Peleus on the practical difficulties in winning over a tricky sea-goddess. As for using magic to prepare a wedding reception, I feel rather insulted that you feel I am incapable of organising suitable arrangements for a wedding reception without resorting to magic. Surely thrones made from trees from Pelion's forests are more in keeping with a marriage between a mortal and a sea-nymph, rather than some grand array of golden thrones created by magical illusion?"

"You are, of course, quite right. I didn't mean any insult to your undoubted abilities, dear Cheiron. Of course not. All I meant was that, if you found it rather a strain to carry out what needs to be done in a mere four days, then you could cheat a little if needs be. That was all. No offence meant."

"No offence taken," said Cheiron, with a smile. Iris looked relieved.

"I'll be off then," she said. "And I'll pop down from time to time over the next few days, just in case there are any revisions to the plans, or in case you have any queries."

"We'll need fine weather for all that has to be done," said Cheiron, "so don't make it too often, there's a dear."

And Iris was gone in an instant, complete with rainbow and rain-cloud. Cheiron trotted off towards the woods, to give preliminary instructions (as I found out later) to some of the wood folk to get cracking on the preparations for the wedding reception.

I turned back into the secret passage, rolled the boulder back into position and returned to my bed.

As I lay there, I pondered on what had caused such a curious turn of events. What gave the gods such an intense interest in Thetis and a desire to marry her off to a mortal such as Peleus?

I also wondered at Cheiron. I had always admired him for the depth of his understanding and the breadth of his skills. Now I reflected on his ability to hobnob with a goddess as an equal and the relaxed way in which he accepted tasks that would have daunted a mere mortal.

Later, at supper, I expected Cheiron might make an announcement which would make things clearer. However, all he said before we left the dining-room for bed was that he had an announcement of great importance which he would make after prayers at morning assembly.

7

Cheiron gives a lesson in mythology

Cheiron was silent and thoughtful at breakfast next day (the third before my birthday). But after prayers at morning assembly, he did not dismiss the school to their lessons but told everyone to sit down.

He told the assembly that he intended to give a lesson on current mythology, instead of the normal first lesson-period of the day.

"I know that most of you are by now fairly well acquainted with early, mediaeval, and modern mythology," he started, "but recent events demand that I inform you of developments in current mythology which are likely to affect all of us during the next few days."

Peleus, who was sitting next to me, yawned. He covered his mouth with his hand, because it would have been unwise to let Cheiron see any sign of lack of interest when he was taking a class lesson in person. Peleus still had not recovered from his encounter with Thetis, and his eyes retained their glassy and far-distant appearance.

"You all will remember," continued Cheiron, "that Poseidon received the empire of the seas from his brother Zeus, and that Nereus, the sage and ancient sea-god, retired gracefully, and somewhat thankfully, to his palace beneath the waves, not far from the eastern shores of our Pelion peninsula. To add to his good fortune, his fifty glamorous daughters, the sea-nymphs known as Nereids, were pleased to look after his well-being and entertain him with their superb dancing.

"One day, several months ago, Poseidon apparently paid a social visit on Nereus, just to see if he was happy, and, possibly, to ascertain whether Nereus was harbouring any seeds of discontent at having his authority overshadowed by Zeus's gift of the empire to his brother.

"However, Nereus welcomed Poseidon and entertained him lavishly. He got his daughters to perform their usual dances for him, and, as the highlight, got his youngest and fairest daughter Thetis to dance a special dance of her own.

"This proved a mistake, because Poseidon immediately took a very strong fancy to her. When he asked Nereus for permission to marry her, Nereus refused, saying that such a marriage was destined to disaster. Poseidon was somewhat upset (to put it mildly) by this refusal but, out of respect for Nereus, he agreed to a cooling-off period, before approaching Nereus again.

"Then Poseidon made a mistake. He boasted to his brother Zeus that he had found the most beautiful and desirable woman in the world or heavens, and, of course, Zeus immediately wanted to see Thetis for himself. So, in suitable disguise, he shimmered down to the bay where the Nereids were in the habit of enjoying their leisure by dancing and singing. And, inevitably, he too fell for the irresistible sea-nymph.

"Sir!" interrupted one of the fifth-years. "Please sir, is that what's wrong with Peleus, sir? Because there's a rumour going round that Peleus saw Thetis herself the other night, and you said she was irresistible, sir!"

"You're not supposed to know about that, young Castor," replied Cheiron, irritably. "No, I was wrong. Thetis is not completely irresistible. It's just that she appeals strongly to certain types of males. And don't worry about Peleus. His indisposition is purely temporary, I assure you."

"No it isn't," mumbled Peleus in my ear. "It damn well isn't."

"To continue," said Cheiron. "When Zeus made advances to Thetis, she rejected them vehemently. One of the reasons for this, I believe, was that Hera, Zeus's wife, had brought up Thetis as a child, and Thetis, of course, did not want to upset Hera by having an affair with her husband. Perhaps you remember from your studies in mythology that Hera was not a good goddess to upset, and was likely to bear grudges for a very long time.

"However, Zeus, being Zeus, was not inclined to give up so easily, particularly as Poseidon was still proclaiming a keen interest in Thetis, and was virtually defying his brother by boasting of his passion for the sea-nymph.

"In fact the situation was beginning to look decidedly ugly when the goddess Themis appeared on the scene. It so happened that Zeus and Hera were entertaining Poseidon socially one day. They were having a sultry meal together and conversation was proving difficult, as you can imagine, when Themis suddenly appeared at the table—she seldom waited to be invited—she usually just appeared."

"Sir!" interrupted another of the fifth-years. "Please sir, we haven't done Themis in class yet, sir! Who was she and what gave her the right to barge in on some of the other gods like that?"

"I'm sorry, young Polydeuces," replied Cheiron. "Let me

explain. Themis is the goddess of Justice and Law and Order. In fact she is usually recognised by a set of portable scales which she carries round with her, allegedly so that she can weigh both sides of an argument. She is one of the Titans (surely you've done them, haven't you?) and is daughter of Uranus (Heaven) and Gaia (Earth), and is highly respected by all the other gods. She is the mother of Prometheus, and, like him, she is endowed with a strong power of prophesy. With Zeus, she presides over all the divine assemblies of the gods. Nobody would dare accuse her of bad manners when she arrives without warning or apology. Are you clear, now?"

"Yes, thank you, sir!" replied young Polydeuces.

"Well, Themis thanked the other three deities for inviting her to supper," continued Cheiron, "but said she couldn't stop. She said she had received a prophesy from her son, Prometheus, which she confirmed herself, namely that a certain sea-nymph called Thetis was fated to bear a son who would be more powerful than his father and who would wield weapons more fearsome than thunderbolts or tridents.

"If it was possible for gods to turn pale, then that is what Zeus and Poseidon did at that moment. In fact they were speechless. Themis continued to say that she thought it was about time that her son, Prometheus, was released from being chained to his rock, particularly since his prophesy, if acted upon, would certainly prevent the present company from a fate worse than she couldn't think what. Zeus apparently nodded in dumbstruck agreement, and Themis slipped away to tell her son the good news."

"Hurrah! Hurrah! Hurrah!" cried the assembled school, both pupils and teachers and domestics. "Prometheus is free at last!" cried Endeis, to be followed by the whole school shouting in unison: "Prometheus is free, Prometheus is free!"

"That's enough!" shouted Cheiron above the din. "Quietly, there, please! Settle down! I am glad you are pleased about the news concerning Prometheus, but I really must continue.

"Hera apparently had a brainwave, which she was sure would solve the whole situation. She pointed out the obvious: if Thetis married *any* god, their offspring would be a terrible threat to the present powers and authority, not only of Zeus and Poseidon, but of all the other gods as well. So she suggested that Thetis, though a goddess and immortal, should be married off as soon as possible to a *mortal*. When asked to suggest a suitable mortal, she suggested someone who had the reputation of being very pious."

Cheiron paused for dramatic effect and I took the opportunity of looking at Peleus. He was looking as though he was about to explode. He muttered to me, "I'll give him 'pious' whoever he is. I'll kill the bastard, I really will. Thetis is mine, I tell you!"

"And whom did Hera choose to be wedded to Thetis?" asked Endeis, on behalf of the assembled school.

"Why, young Peleus here, of course," replied Cheiron, and sat down for a short rest.

8

Cheiron gets things sorted

In the silence which followed Cheiron's announcement, I tried to count the number of different emotions which must have been swimming around in Peleus's breast at that moment. I must confess, I gave up, mainly because Chariclo shouted at me to get a flask containing Cheiron's marvellous *Rescue Remedy* for administration to our pious hero.

It worked like a charm. Within a few minutes, Peleus was like his old self again, much to the relief of the whole school.

"When? When? When?" cried Peleus, and Cheiron, with due solemnity, rose to speak again.

"Yesterday, as young Jason here may have told a few of you in confidence, I had a visit from Iris herself, who, as you may know, is the personal messenger of the goddess Hera."

I asked myself how Cheiron could possibly have known I was listening in on his conversation with Iris, but failed, as usual, to answer such a question.

Cheiron then went on to recount most of the details of Iris's instructions.

"And so," he continued, "the programme is as follows: Today you will have your usual lessons. Tomorrow, the whole school, apart from the nursery department and the kindergarten, will be going on an expedition which, I assure you, will be the experience of your lifetimes. And then, on the next day, the day before the great wedding itself, you will all be very busy getting the school premises and the playground ready for the reception and getting yourselves washed and groomed."

"Where *are* we going tomorrow, sir?" asked one of the fourth-formers.

"You will find out soon enough," replied Cheiron. "And now, off to your lessons, and no more questions."

Cheiron beckoned to Peleus and me to stay behind. Peleus was full of excitement now, and wanted to be off straightaway to the east coast to lie in wait for Thetis.

"Oh no you don't, young Peleus," said Cheiron when he came over to us. He led us out into the playground and told us to sit down.

"Listen carefully, you two," he continued. "I have a lot to do today. I must go again into the forests and talk to all the forest-folk—the dryads, the naiads, the oreads, and all the other nymphs and forest animals—to give them final detailed instructions in what will be required for the wedding-feast at the time of the full moon three days hence. It may be magic or it may not be (who knows?) but all that is required can be conjured up by them to ensure that the feast will not fall short of what the gods will surely expect of us. Music and food and wine and garlands and even thrones will, I assure you, be such that you will never experience the like again."

Cheiron paused, and I could see that the whole scene of the gathering of the gods for the wedding was vivid in his mind.

He continued, "For many years now I have felt that an occasion like this—the gathering here of the gods of

34

Olympus—was destined to take place. So on all my excursions into the forests of Pelion, I have made frequent contact with the many nymphs and birds and beasts of the forest. I have acquainted myself with their many skills and now those skills will be employed to the full for the full-moon wedding feast—your wedding in fact young Peleus.

"While I am away, you have a lot to do. Peleus must prepare himself for tomorrow's encounter with Thetis. Yes, Peleus, your *encounter* with Thetis. You must prepare yourself for a struggle, the like of which you will never experience again. Thetis, as an immortal, is endowed with skills which are designed to protect her from all dangers. She can turn herself at will into any form she chooses— beast or bird, fire or water. You must grasp her and hold on to her and not let go whatever form she takes. If you let go, you have lost her. However, the time will come when even she will tire. Provided you have not let go your hold on her, she will almost certainly submit and only then will she be yours.

"I suggest you both go down to Jason's farm. Peleus can practise holding on to one of Jason's bulls and then one of his stallions and then one of his boars. I suggest you aim for an hour on each.

"And you, young Jason, can take that smile off your face, cover yourself with grease and let Peleus practise wrestling with *you* for an hour or so. Right then—off you go and when I come back this evening, I expect to see Peleus tired out and resting in order to recuperate ready for our trip to the east coast tomorrow, because that is when Peleus must win his bride. I am letting the school come with us;

35

it will be a historic moment in mythology which I want all our future heroes to witness and remember. So don't let me down!"

"I most certainly won't let you down, sir," replied Peleus. "Tomorrow Thetis will be mine, you'll see!"

"Mmm…" said Cheiron, and trotted off towards the forests.

"Do you really think I *need* to spend all day today practising catching hold of wriggling animals?" asked Peleus, when Cheiron was out of earshot.

"Thank you for thinking of me as a wriggling animal," I replied, "and if Cheiron says you need to practise, then you need to practise. So let's get down to the farm and get on with it."

Which is what we did. Once Peleus started, he soon got into the swing of it. I gave him full marks for tenacity. After an hour with one of my bulls and an hour with one of my stallions, I introduced him to my really bad-tempered boar who strongly objected to being grappled with. In fact, after an hour with Peleus, the old boar seemed to give up and never seemed quite himself thereafter. For years afterwards, whenever Peleus happened to be passing by the farm, the old boar, instead of snorting and preparing to charge, would grunt disdainfully, trot off to a quiet little copse behind the pig-pens and have a lie-down.

When it came to grappling with me, my greasy body (I used beef fat) was almost impossible for Peleus to hold, but somehow he met the challenge and, however much I wriggled, he maintained a continuous, if precarious, hold. By the end of an hour we were both exhausted and staggered back to the school for a hot bath and a rest.

Cheiron arrived back shortly before the evening meal and checked that we had carried out the practice as instructed. He seemed pleased that we had done so, and reported that he had had a very successful day.

"I am sure," he said, "that, with the help of the forest folk, the gods will be pleased with the wedding arrangements. In fact, I had a chat with the centaurs and persuaded them to attend the wedding feast. They promised they would be well behaved for a change. In fact they seemed quite keen to come, for they thought it might clean up their reputation a little in the sight of the gods and the other wedding guests if they could spend the day repressing their inherent bad tempers."

"Isn't it a bit risky?" I asked.

"Not really," replied Cheiron with a grin. "I expect Zeus will bring a few thunderbolts with him and use them if necessary!"

I suppose it was that remark, although made partly in jest, which made me realise the seriousness of the impending gathering of the gods for the wedding ceremony. Only once before had anything like this taken place on earth and among mortals. And now, at our School for Heroes, in a playground on the side of an ordinary mountain range in ancient Greece, we were to attend a wedding between a beautiful goddess and a mortal friend of mine, in the presence, not only of all the major gods of Olympus, but of the great god Zeus himself, complete with thunderbolts.

Scary.

And so we all went in to the school hall for supper, thinking of this and that, and wondering about tomorrow.

9

Peleus versus Thetis at Cape Sepias

Next morning. after breakfast, the whole school, apart from the under-sixes (who stayed behind under the care of Philyra, Cheiron's mother), set off southwards for the east coast of the peninsula. There were twenty-seven of us in all, and we followed the tracks which Peleus and I had used three days previously.

As then, the weather was ideal for the outing. The combination of sun, wispy clouds and cooling breeze made walking down the Pelion ridge an experience which was a pleasant change from normal schooling. I was worried that the youngsters might find a jaunt of over fifteen miles somewhat tiring, but not so; they romped and played touch nearly all the way, which was a credit to Cheiron's policy of bringing them up tough. Obesity was definitely not included in the curriculum!

Peleus was in fine fettle. He kept racing on ahead and then had to wait (very impatiently) for us to catch up. Cheiron insisted that our pace was leisurely. He instilled a relaxed atmosphere into the expedition, and, when we had arrived at the saddle of the ridge from where we had our first glimpse of the Aegean sea, we spent over an hour at noon having a picnic.

By late afternoon we had arrived at the marigold patch overlooking the bay where once again we refreshed ourselves with yet another picnic. Cheiron organised games and contests for all the boys and these continued until the sun set behind the mountain ridge to our west.

The moon rose full in a near-cloudless sky and cast a spell of enchantment over the scene.

Chariclo (Cheiron's wife) and Endeis (his daughter) organised the boys to lie well spaced out along the cliff edge, lying on their fronts, so that they could see down into the bay. By the light of the moon it was unlikely that they could be seen by the Nereids when they swam in for their early evening frolic in the shallow waters and sands of the bay.

Cheiron himself took Peleus aside and gave him stern instructions concerning his impending tussle with Thetis. I could see that Peleus was getting impatient, and, sure enough, as soon as Cheiron let him, he once again slithered down the cliff face and hid himself behind the myrtle-berry bushes to the side of the cave entrance.

I prepared myself for a longish wait and was beginning to worry that the boys might get restless when suddenly the surface of the waters started to quiver as fifty Nereids glided gracefully into the bay below us. Thetis then led some twenty of her sisters onto the beach and there followed one of the most graceful dances I have ever experienced. For years afterwards the boys of Cheiron's school talked about it. Many of them, in spite of their rippling muscles and hairy chests, sometimes asked Cheiron whether ballet dancing could be included in the school syllabus. Cheiron invariably replied that he was mentally and physically unqualified to give the necessary instruction.

Eventually the dance came to an end. The Nereids all retired exhausted back into the sea for a relaxing swim, with the exception of Thetis, who, as she told me later, was in the habit of retiring into her cave for a rest. As she walked past the myrtle-berry bushes, Peleus jumped out from his cover and grasped her tightly in his arms.

What followed happened so suddenly and with the usual lack of clarity which moonlight affords, that I regret I cannot give an exact account. I subsequently questioned both the staff and the boys of the school to obtain a definitive description of all the various guises which Thetis assumed during the time when Peleus was wrestling with her, but although most of the onlookers agreed roughly with what the guises were, they were all confused as to the order in which they happened and how long they lasted.

Certainly the guises included: a column of fire followed (fortunately for Peleus) by a stream of water of such force that it left a deep pit in the sand; a sea-bird with savage beak and claws; a sea-serpent which coiled itself around Peleus so that I wondered how he could breathe; some boys recalled a huge tree-trunk (which I would have thought could have been by way of an intermission for Peleus!); an large cat-like animal which was variously reported as a lion, a spotted tigress and (as *I* remember it) a lithe black panther, which to me seemed the most terrifying of all. Each of these guises seemed to alternate and return, and this perhaps accounts for the varied impressions given to the onlookers.

But definitely the final guise was that of a giant cuttlefish which almost defeated Peleus by thrashing its way out of Peleus's weakening grasp. However, I confess that I had difficulty in suppressing my laughter when the fish started squirting sepia-coloured ink all over Pelias as they tussled together. In fact this incident of the sepia ink so impressed all those who observed it that the arm of land shielding the bay was henceforth named *Cape Sepias*!

This was Thetis's last guise before she quivered back to her Nereid form.

"That's enough for now, Peleus," we heard her say. "You can let go of me now."

Peleus released his grasp and stood back, staring at her in admiration.

"Well," continued Thetis, "aren't you going to ask me to marry you? Ye gods and little fishes, you do look a mess! But perhaps brown ink suits you—it certainly gives you a healthy-looking tan. Are we going to join your friends up there on the cliff, or have I got to stand around here all night? Sorry about the tussle, but you took me by surprise. I hope you're not too tired as a result, though I understand heroes are supposed to have plenty of stamina."

Then turning round to address the other forty-nine Nereids who all this time had been watching the encounter from the bay, she cried, "That's it, dear sisters. Time for you to go home. It looks as though I shall be busy for the next few days or so, but tell Father that everything went according to plan and that I'll visit him after the honeymoon."

Turning to Peleus, who meanwhile had been standing with a look of astonishment on his sepia-coloured face, Thetis said, "Well, come on then, darling, let's get up this wretched cliff and meet all your school-chums."

Very thoughtfully I had tied one end of rope to a tree growing near the cliff edge and thrown the other end down the cliff face. Thetis wasted no time in using this to scale the cliff-face.

Peleus followed dutifully after her.

"There's a spring over there," said Thetis to Peleus when they had both reached the top. "Why don't you walk over and get yourself cleaned up? That sepia stuff will be hell to get off if you leave it too long. Why don't you get Endeis to go with you and scrub the stuff off your back? I can see some good gorse bushes near the spring which will serve as a brush."

Peleus uttered his first words since before the Nereids had arrived. "Yes dear. I'll not be long." Endeis took the hint and went with him.

Thetis walked up to Cheiron and me, while Chariclo organised the boys into getting themselves ready to have a picnic before returning back to the school.

"This is Jason," said Cheiron introducing me to Thetis.

"I know," replied Thetis. "He comes and watches me and my sisters quite often during the school holidays. Hello, young Jason," she said, turning to me. "I've heard a lot about you. I hope you'll be a good friend to me as well as to Peleus in the years to come. Things won't always be easy, and you and Peleus have many adventures ahead of you. But remember this: Hera and I and other goddesses will always be somewhere around to help you when the going gets tough."

Cheiron was smiling. "That all went off very well, didn't it?" he said to Thetis. "I'm sure the boys will remember your magic illusions for their life-times and pass versions of it on to their descendants for many generations to come. How *do* you do it?"

"It's a girl's prerogative to play hard-to-get any which way she can," replied Thetis, laughing. "Why not leave it at that?"

"Then let us join the others and have a bite to eat," said Cheiron.

And so we all had a moonlight picnic. Peleus soon came back looking sore but somewhat cleaner, and he sat down with Thetis. He had obviously recovered now from his ordeal because, from what I could observe at a distance, he was starting to get an occasional word in edgeways.

Cheiron said to me, "Don't you worry about those two, young Jason. They will have little time for anyone except each other until after the wedding at least."

"Aren't you being rather cynical, sir?" I responded.

"Peleus will need your friendship more than ever now. A mortal cannot marry a non-mortal without incurring marital problems. Maybe one day you'll need Peleus's friendship even more than he needs yours now. Who knows?"

"I bet *you* do," I thought to myself.

Cheiron smiled and said, "Right then, everybody! It's time to get back to school. It's a long way, so we'll take it steadily."

And then Cheiron did something which I had never known him do before. He invited Thetis to get on his back for the journey home. "I'll remind you all," he said grimly to all around him, "that I am *not* a horse, and that I am merely offering to carry a goddess on my back as a matter of courtesy."

Thetis refused his offer with grace, saying that the walk would do her good after so much swimming recently.

And so, after I had completed a careful count of the whole party to ensure that no one was missing, we all walked steadily back to the school, bathed in silvery moonlight. It had been a day to remember.

10

Preparations for the wedding

The problem with the next day—the day before my birthday and the wedding of Peleus and Thetis—was that there was a lot to be done by way of preparation (for the wedding) and that practically everyone wanted to sleep. We did, in fact, arrive back at the school a little before dawn. Cheiron announced a compromise: everyone would go to bed and sleep (or try to sleep) until noon, at which time the gong would sound and everyone would be given their instructions.

Thetis was offered Philyra's room to herself, but refused, saying she would be quite happy to share the room with her, sleeping on a mattress in a corner. Philyra protested, saying that the mattress was probably damp, but Thetis said she was used to damp beds, thank you all the same. "In any case," said Thetis, "Philyra is the daughter of Oceanus, the father of all rivers, so, speaking as a Nereid, I'm sure we have a lot in common, and it will be pleasant to have an opportunity for plenty of girl-talk."

Peleus and I, being mere mortals, were not in the mood for talking all night, and we slept soundly. Peleus seemed to be suffering from tiredness and mixed emotions, which was not surprising, considering the events of the previous day. I was just weary and, I confess, relaxed; after all Peleus seemed to have got what he wanted, which was a relief. He had been rather obsessed most of the week, and this had been more than a little tiresome.

I was in the middle of a dream in which I was trying unsuccessfully to run a farm consisting mainly of savage sea-serpents, black panthers and giant cuttlefish which were squirting me with sepia ink, when the boom of the school gong awoke me.

"Assembly-time! In the playground today!" cried Cheiron. "Come along, quickly there, and settle down!"

When we looked around us, we could see an almost incredible transformation of the playground. The forest-folk, the dryads, the naiads, the oreads and all the other nymphs and forest animals, had transformed the playground. The surface was no longer a practical gravel but was now a bright green springy turf, suitable for the most respectable garden party.

Where we were standing, immediately in front of the main school entrance, there was an oval space suitable for dancing. Everywhere else there were tables and couches. The tables were in long well spaced rows across the playground and between them were couches so that guests could recline on them and chat to each other while still able to reach the tables. As yet there was no food or drink that I could see.

As I turned to listen to Cheiron, who was standing with his back to the school, I could see that there were what looked like thrones arrayed to his left and right. They were certainly magnificent, fit for a god or goddess to sit on, carved from oak and decorated with leaves and spring flowers of every kind. I was half-expecting thrones of gold and silver, but these were much more beautiful. The forest-folk had obviously been very hard at work.

I was in a daze of admiration. I was counting them and had got to seven when Cheiron's voice boomed, "Twelve, young Jason, and stop counting things when you should be paying attention to what I am saying!"

"All the food and drink are stored in the cool of the school larder," he continued. "Today, under the supervision of Philyra, Chariclo and Endeis, you will decorate all the tables and couches, and tomorrow morning, at dawn, you will array all the food and drink on the tables. There will be no rain, except a little local shower nearby when Iris arrives.

"Twelve thrones have been provided by the forest folk, because twelve gods and goddesses have accepted the invitations to the wedding. We are expecting them to arrive about noon tomorrow, so you will have the morning to put the last-minute touches to the decorations.

"Some of you have asked which of the gods will be coming, and I suppose there is no harm in telling you now. In fact, it will stop you goggling tomorrow as they arrive, and pestering the school staff about their names. It should be obvious which is which, if you have been attending to your mythology lessons, and you will be given a test in the near future on what you have learnt about the gods from your observations tomorrow.

"Originally Iris said that we could expect the twelve Olympian gods and goddesses. Zeus and Hera will be coming, and these two central thrones, on my left and right, are for them, of course. Apollo and Artemis will not be coming; for some reason or other they have sent their apologies. Aphrodite will be here, but has said that her husband Hephaestus will not be coming; his leg is hurting him and, in any case, he's not in the mood. Two other goddesses will be present: Athena, daughter of Zeus and patron of war, and Demeter, the great Mother goddess of the Earth. Poseidon, Zeus's brother and the god of the sea, is coming. Then there is Ares, who is the son of Zeus and Hera, and you may remember is also the god of war; so look out some of you. Hermes, who is Zeus's messenger, and son of Zeus and Maia has also accepted. Let me see, now, that makes nine who are coming so far."

"I make it eight, so far, sir," I said.

"I'm sure you are right," said Cheiron, not without some tone of annoyance. "Then there is Dionysus, the god of wine and mystic ecstasy. That makes nine, as I said just now. So, due to the non-acceptances of Apollo, Artemis and Hephaestus, Iris asked Hera whom she should invite to fill the customary twelve thrones.

"And Hera suggested the following: Iris herself (a very tactful move on Hera's part, I think). Amphitrite, Poseidon's wife and daughter of Nereus, and a sea-goddess. And lastly Prometheus, who, as I told you a few days ago, was recently released from being chained to his rock when he advised Zeus not to marry Thetis."

This last announcement was greeted with a cheer, because, as I have said, the whole school regarded Prometheus as a hero.

"Do not," Cheiron continued, "show your favouritism

towards any particular god or goddess tomorrow. I believe Zeus approved the invitation to Prometheus as a gesture of goodwill. But use your common sense tomorrow. We don't want Zeus losing his temper and throwing his thunderbolts around. It would create the wrong sort of atmosphere, would it not?"

"Yes, sir," came a chorus of voices from the assembled school of potential heroes.

"Right then. Off you go and get decorating. I want this playground to look like a banqueting hall fit for the gods. Pay attention to what Philyra, Chariclo and Endeis tell you, otherwise heaven knows what the result will be."

Surprisingly, the rest of the day went smoothly, and by the time we went to bed, the playground had been transformed. Even Cheiron was impressed.

Peleus was definitely jumpy. "It's all right for you," he said to me before I dropped off to sleep, "you're not marrying a goddess tomorrow, are you?"

"I thought that was what you wanted," I said.

"Well, yes," he replied.

11

The wedding of Peleus and Thetis

Rosy-fingered dawn crept stealthily over Pelion's ridge and streaked the Pagasitic gulf before us with gold while the school playground was still shrouded in shadow. It was the day of my fourteenth birthday, and I sensed it would be a day to remember.

After an early breakfast, while the playground was still shaded and cool, Cheiron called assembly and outlined the day ahead.

"This morning, you will all, with the exception of Peleus and Thetis, arrange all the food and drink on these tables, and, under the supervision of Philyra, Chariclo and Endeis, put the finishing touches to this festival arena. You have only until noon. Remember this: the great gods of Olympus are honouring the wedding with their presence. There has been only one wedding like it before—that of Cadmus and Harmonia, who, as you may remember from your mythology lessons, is the daughter of Ares and Aphrodite, both of whom will be arriving here soon. No doubt they will compare the arrangements of that wedding with your efforts now, so please do your very best, and don't let the school down.

"The programme for today is as follows:

"Any time after noon, you can expect the guests to arrive in any order. The forest-folk will be here, not only as guests but also to ensure that everything is in order and to carry out running repairs. Ganymede will no doubt be accompanying Zeus as his cup-bearer. Orpheus is coming to be in charge of the music and he will be backed up by the nine muses. Also, you will no doubt be pleased to see again all of Thetis's sisters, the Nereids, who are coming to lead the dancing. And you may not believe this, but the Centaurs have promised to behave themselves for the day; they intend to enjoy the occasion, although, at their own suggestion, because of their size, they have agreed to remain on the outskirts of the playground.

"The afternoon will be spent in feasting and entertainment, but the actual wedding ceremony will not take place until this evening, when the full moon rises at sunset. When Hera considers that the time is right, she will perform the marriage rites, after which the feasting will continue until the gods tire and retire. Any questions?"

"Please, sir," asked one of the lower school, "will the gods and goddesses sit on their thrones all the time?"

"I should hope not," replied Cheiron. "They will mingle with all of us, and recline on whichever couch takes their fancy, and eat and drink to their hearts' content, like the rest of us. Try to be grown-up today, even if you are not."

"Please, sir," asked one of the seniors, "are we allowed to drink as much wine as we want?"

Cheiron smiled and replied, "You may drink as much wine as you want and think you can cope with without getting drunk and letting the reputation of the school down. Otherwise you will suffer from a sore head tomorrow morning in more ways than one.

"Any more questions?" he continued. There were none, and we were dismissed to carry out the final preparations for the feast.

Noon soon came and the guests started to arrive. There were so many of them that I cannot possibly describe the manner of their arrival. As for the gods and goddesses, no one, as far as I remember, saw any one of them actually *arrive*. In any case, Cheiron had ordered me to accompany Peleus closely to make sure he did not get drunk before the ceremony, and, if possible, afterwards as well. So my chances of observing and remembering all that went on were remote.

Certainly by early afternoon the playground was packed with reclining guests, both divine and otherwise, all of whom were obviously enjoying themselves immensely. And they did not stick to one particular couch or table. Wanting to meet as many of the other guests as possible, they circulated freely.

The atmosphere was full of goodwill and jollity. The gods and goddesses surprised me with how freely they laughed and enjoyed themselves, and this put all the other guests at their ease. Dionysus seemed to be in charge of the wine, some of which he had apparently brought with him, and this proved both abundant and popular, and was, no doubt, helpful to the relaxed atmosphere which pervaded the festivities.

But I am sure it was the presence of Orpheus which had the most dramatic effect upon the proceedings. I had learnt from my lessons that Orpheus was so superb a musician that, when he sang and played his lyre, all nature became entranced. Combined with the magic of the dancing displays by the Nereids (with Thetis herself in the lead), his music supplied an atmosphere so surreal that it defeats my ability to describe it.

My head was swimming with the magic of his music, and, I confess, with perhaps too much wine, when I felt a tap on my shoulder. As I turned I realised that it was Hera herself who had tapped it.

"Hello, young Jason," said Hera, wife of Zeus and queen of Heaven. "Not a bad party you've helped to arrange here today. Well done, and thank you, by the way, for helping Peleus with his courtship. It was, of course, essential that Thetis marry him. I don't need to tell you why!

"I hear through the grapevine that you would make a good accountant, but I have other plans for you. We don't want you to waste all your time at this school for heroes if you aren't going to try to be one, do we? You've six more years here, I understand from Cheiron, after which we'll have another chat. I can be very patient, even where that rat Pelias is concerned. Goodbye for now!"

Hera laughed as she walked away, but her expression was, I thought, a trifle sinister. "Why had she mentioned Pelias, my father's half-brother and enemy?" I asked myself. Perhaps Cheiron would know; he seemed to know most things.

But I had little time to ponder further. I was kept busy by following Peleus around; he seemed determined to get himself congratulated by as many of the guests as possible. He even had the temerity to introduce himself to Zeus, who said, "Congratulations, young Peleus. I hope you enjoy yourself as much as I would have done, but watch your offspring—they may be tricky! Goodbye." And Peleus had the good sense to move on.

In no time at all, so it seemed, dusk arrived and a full moon started to rise in an almost cloudless sky. The gods and goddesses took their places on their respective thrones. Hera came forward and called upon Peleus and Thetis to join her in the clear space where the dancing had been. The ceremony was solemn and simple in the extreme. Sacrifices were dispensed with, since most of the gods were present anyway. Hera sprinkled water over the bride and bridegroom who then made their vows under Hera's instructions. Aphrodite and Demeter came forward from their thrones and gave their blessings to the union, and that was that. The other gods then came down from their thrones and congratulated the happy couple in turn.

Then, when the gods had returned to their thrones, Cheiron came forward to make an announcement.

"I understand," he said, "that now is time for presents to be given to the bride and groom, and I call upon…"

"Eris!" called a shrill voice from behind him. "Eris, goddess of Strife, is here with her present! But not for the bride or groom. I know I was not invited to this wedding, but here I am anyway. I'm not staying, so don't get too upset, but here is a present for one of the goddesses here today."

Whereupon she rolled a golden apple across the lawn and disappeared. The apple came to rest at the feet of Peleus who stooped and picked it up.

"Give it here," thundered Zeus, and Peleus immediately walked over to his throne and gave it to him.

Zeus inspected it slowly, appeared to read some writing on it and hesitated.

"Well, what does it say?" demanded Hera.

"It says *'To the fairest'*," replied Zeus, and immediately Hera, Aphrodite and Athena left their thrones and stood before him, hands outstretched.

"Well, I know to whom *I* would give it," he said, winking at Hera, "but, then, I'm prejudiced. I think the best plan is for me to appoint an independent arbiter, when I can find one, and let him or her decide to whom it should be given. In the meantime, we shall continue with these excellent festivities and not let Eris achieve her objective in creating strife where there should be harmony. So please return to your thrones, fair ladies, and let the presentations commence."

For a few moments the three goddesses seemed to be reluctant to move until a clap of thunder overhead sent them scurrying back to their seats.

Cheiron heaved a sigh of relief and asked those who had gifts for the bride and groom to come forward. Cheiron himself gave Peleus a magnificent spear, heavy and huge and strong; it had been cut from an ash tree on the summit of Mount Pelion, Athena had polished its shaft, and Hephaestus had forged its blade. The joint gift from the gods was a suit of armour which was a wonder to behold. Poseidon presented two immortal horses which I later discovered were named Balius and Xanthus, horses which the harpy Podarge had conceived to Zephyrus, the West Wind, as she grazed on the meadow beside the stream of Oceanus. All these gifts were destined to find fame on the plains of Troy in years to come—but that is another story. Thetis too had many gifts from the gods, from her sisters and the forest folk, but I must confess that I was so busy dealing with the gifts to Peleus (particularly trying to find suitable temporary stabling for the horses) that I cannot remember much about them.

The festivities ended some time in the early hours of the morning. The gods and goddesses went as they came; one moment they were there and the next moment they were not. The forest folk drifted off home in happy groups. The centaurs, before they left, came from the edges of the playground and did a circuit of the dancing area, their heads crowned with leaves and each with a lance of pine, and were applauded for their unusual taste and restraint. Peleus and Thetis rode on Balius and Xanthus back to Thetis's cave at Cape Sepias where they intended to spend their honeymoon. They were accompanied by the Nereids who said they were going that way anyway.

Cheiron ordered the pupils to bed well before the end of the festivities but allowed me to stay up later until I had helped Peleus and Thetis on to their horses and wished them well on their journey.

When I did get to bed, I could not sleep. After tossing and turning for a while on my mattress, I crept to my secret tunnel into the deserted playground, climbed in the moonlight to my favourite spot on the slope above the school where there was an unobstructed view over the whole Pagasitic gulf.

I brooded over the events of the previous day. The wedding had gone well in spite of the attempt of Eris to disrupt the happy atmosphere. Peleus had behaved himself well and had avoided having accidents, apart from marrying Thetis (and that thought, I confess, brought a grin to my face).

But then my thoughts turned to Hera, and what she had said to me. She had referred to "that rat Pelias". According to Cheiron he was my bad uncle who had cheated my father Aeson out of the throne of Iolcos, but what had he done to upset Hera and what had it got to do with me?

There was a tap on my shoulder, and I nearly jumped out of my skin.

"You'll have to wait and see," said Cheiron who had crept up behind me with a brace of hares over his shoulder. "I could not sleep either, and I needed exercise. But it's time to try to get some sleep now, and we must return to our beds."

As we neared the school, I said to Cheiron, "By the way, sir, yesterday was my fourteenth birthday."

"Was it really?" responded Cheiron. "Well, congratulations, young Jason! You certainly had a party to end all parties, didn't you?"

"And by the way," he continued without waiting for my reply, "how many were there in total, including centaurs and forest folk, at yesterday's party?"

"Three hundred and sixty-five, sir," I replied as we crept back into the school.

12

The next six years

We did not see or hear from Peleus for fourteen days, so we presumed (correctly) that he was busy with enjoying his honeymoon.

Then, on the fifteenth day after the big wedding, he came limping across the playground at supper-time. Of course a meal and wine was instantly set before him and he joined me at my table.

"What's wrong with your leg," I asked him.

"Nothing much," he replied, "except that I tripped over several tree roots when I took a short-cut through one of the woods."

"There are no short-cuts through the woods," I commented.

"So I discovered," he said, "so shut up about my leg. Put some of your stinking ointment on it after supper, if you must, and don't bother to ask me how my marriage is getting on."

"You *are* in a mood," I replied. "And how *is* your marriage getting on?"

"Fine!" he said, "Fine! Except that she's gone off back home to Dad for ten days or so, to get a rest, so she says. Anyway, we've come to an agreement. She's going to live most of the time at home with her father and sisters, and I can do what I like, and we will spend a few nights together every ten days or so. That way, she says, our marriage may work. She reckons the problem is that she is a goddess and immortal whereas I am very mortal, and that this creates problems of compatibility. I think I know what she means, and I've agreed to go along with it. So I've come back here for ten days, and in some ways I am looking forward to it. Anyway, I need a holiday."

"You're very welcome, young Peleus," said Cheiron, who had been listening (like everyone else present). "The arrangement seems admirable, and we need a sixth-former like you with experience in hunting and athletics who can give tuition to the lower school."

"And I could do with some help down on the farm," I said. "The fresh air will do you good after that stuffy cave."

Peleus looked relieved that he had received a welcome-back to the school, and had Cheiron's approval to his marriage arrangement.

And for the next five years, that's what happened. Peleus spent most of his time at the school with visits to his wife in the cave at cape Sepias every ten days or so.

But married life was not easy for Peleus. He said he enjoyed his visits to his wife and he said he loved her and that she loved him, but there was a problem—a big problem.

Thetis became pregnant six times during the five years, and Peleus managed almost always to be present at the birth of his offspring, which happened to be all boys. But they did not survive. Peleus said that Thetis gave them much love and attention while he was away at school, but they would die suddenly within a month of their birth. Thetis said that they were cot-deaths and that none of her friends could suggest a remedy. Cheiron was asked for his opinion, but he replied that paediatrics was not his specialty, and why didn't Peleus spend more time with the babies, at least for the first few months? Peleus said that Thetis told him not to fuss, that she was quite capable of looking after her own children, and if Peleus did not trust her and wanted to break their marriage arrangements, he could forget all about their marriage.

Peleus became more and more gloomy but was obviously afraid of upsetting Thetis. But after the sixth cot-death, he said he had had enough.

"Thetis is pregnant for the seventh time," he said to me. "When the time comes and she has given birth, I intend to sneak back to the cave frequently, and observe how well she is nursing the baby. It won't be the first time I have slipped down the cliff and hidden behind the myrtle-berry bushes."

The time did come, and Thetis gave birth to another boy. Peleus stayed with her for fourteen days, helping her nurse the child. But then he came back to the school and told me he intended to carry out his plan straightaway to return to the cave and watch Thetis without her knowing.

He asked me to accompany him, because he said he might need some help. Of course I agreed, with Cheiron's permission, and I set off with Peleus, carrying my usual shoulder-bag of provisions, first-aid items and the essential rope.

We arrived at the cliff-top above the cave at dusk. The sky was cloudless and moon was rising, which was fortunate. I would have hated not to have been able to watch the cave entrance for any activity.

Peleus slithered down the rope with his usual agility, and I could see him hiding behind the myrtle-berry bushes and peering into the cave.

For some time nothing happened. But suddenly I heard Peleus shriek and saw him disappear into the cave. Then voices, angry voices, came echoing out of the cave. Soon I saw Thetis's sisters swarming into the bay in great agitation. Then Thetis came storming out of the cave shrieking inaudibly, waving her arms, hair swirling round her head and shoulders. Her sisters cried out to her and gathered round her in great concern. And then they were gone and there was a terrifying silence broken only by the crying of a baby and the deep groans of Peleus.

I had tied the rope to a tree-root, and I wasted no time in clawing my way down the cliff-face to join Peleus at the cave entrance. He was holding the baby tenderly in his arms and rocking it to and fro, and crying as I had never seen a man cry before.

I kept silence for a while, merely placing my hand on his shoulder. Eventually he stopped crying and looked at me as though he was glad I was there.

"Come on, Peleus," I said. "Just sit down and tell me what happened. Take your time."

He did, but in due course he gave me the baby to nurse and spoke softly.

"I have no idea whether I have done right or wrong," he said. "No idea at all. But I just couldn't help reacting the way I did. She was holding the baby in the fire there, and letting the flames wrap round it! My baby. In the fire. So I snatched it from her grip and got it away from the fire. Well, what else would you have done?"

"The same as you did, of course," I replied. "But when you took it from her, did you ask her what she thought she was doing?"

"Of course I did," Peleus said. "It was difficult to understand completely what she was saying, because she was stamping her foot and screaming at me all the time, but she said she was trying to make him immortal. She said it had worked with the other six babies and they were all now on Olympus. She said she had taken him to the River Styx (can you believe it?) and dipped him in it, to make him invulnerable everywhere except the heel by which she had held him. To complete the treatment, she said that she was anointing him with ambrosia by day and burning him in the fire by night in order to burn away the mortality which he had inherited from me. And, she said it was all my fault for being a mortal, and if I could do any better I had better get on with it. She reminded me of our marriage oaths, particularly the one where I promised not to question her divine rights. And with that she stormed out, as you saw. So here I am, left holding the baby."

I did not think it would be tactful to remind him that the baby was being held by me. I looked at it carefully, expecting it to be suffering from burns which I could treat from the first-aid kit in my shoulder-bag. But there was no sign of burning. In fact his skin appeared to be glowing, but not as the result of his immersion in the fire. I remarked on this to Peleus, who said it must be the protection afforded by the ambrosia treatment.

"Did Thetis say whether or not the treatment was complete?" I asked Peleus.

"Oh dear," he replied. "Yes, she said my interference halfway through meant that he was invulnerable, apart from his heel, but not immortal. To achieve immortality would require several more days of the ambrosia and fire treatment."

"Do you intend to continue with it?" I asked him.

"You must be joking," he replied. "I couldn't possibly hold a baby in a fire, and in any case, how do you think I can get hold of any ambrosia? Don't tell me you carry it in your bag of tricks, do you?"

"No I don't," I said, "and if you're going to be silly, I suggest we get out of here and get this baby back to the school so that Cheiron and his ladies can give him a check-over. Because I don't know what to do with babies, and neither do you."

"All right," said Peleus. "Don't get huffy. Let's get going then."

Which is what we did. Up the cliff we climbed, followed by yet another moonlit walk back to school. Only this time we were taking it in turns to carry a burbling baby in our arms.

We arrived back at school with the dawn (rosy-fingered as usual). Cheiron was waiting for us.

"What have you two got there?" he asked.

61

"Peleus's latest baby," I replied, and went on to describe what had happened back at the cave.

"And what is the baby's name?" asked Cheiron.

Peleus and I looked at each other with equally vacant expressions.

"His name," said Cheiron, "you pair of nitwits, is, of course, *Achilles.*"

And that was that.

13

My twentieth birthday

Here in the Elysian Fields, Achilles needs no prompting to recite Homer's *Iliad*, describing his exploits on the plains of Troy. Fortunately we do not have to listen unless we feel inclined.

Back at Cheiron's school, Peleus and I had no idea of what the future held for baby Achilles.

We asked Cheiron several times to give us a few clues. All he would say is "Who knows?" In answer to which we thought (but did not say) "We bet you do!"

Achilles was accepted as a pupil and received special attention from the staff. Cheiron devised new special diets for him, because, as Cheiron said, he was not destined to become one of our usual run-of-the-mill heroes.

However, babies are babies, and since I was nineteen years old and knew I probably had to leave soon after my twentieth birthday, I had other things on my mind. Also Peleus was very approximately twenty-one and was beginning to get restless. He no longer had the marriage tie of visiting Thetis's cave at Cape Sepias from time to time, and he began to wonder whether he should return to Phthia and try his luck there again with King Eurytion and his daughter Antigone.

Cheiron advised against this for a year or two. He told Peleus that he would probably first be needed by me in the near future, and he advised him to wait and see.

And so for the remainder of my twentieth year I continued with my education, though I spent most of my time on the farm. Peleus seemed happy continuing with his teaching lessons in hunting and athletics and helping me from time to time with the crops and the animals. And so we spent the winter months pleasantly enough, though I was restless with wondering what kind of adventure was obviously in store for me. Cheiron stubbornly refused to give any more hints.

And then the day before my twentieth birthday arrived. I approached Cheiron and demanded to know what kind of celebrations there would be to mark an occasion which for me was obviously of considerable significance.

"I'm glad you asked me that," said Cheiron, "because tomorrow there is going to be a festival in Iolcos, and you are invited to attend in person. Yes, another celebration for you, young Jason, and one which you will be able to remember in times to come.

"The occasion, which happens fortuitously to coincide with your twentieth birthday, is a festival in the marketplace on the sea-front of Iolcos which has been organised by your uncle Pelias. A sacrifice will be made to Poseidon who is, you may remember from your mythology lessons, Pelias's father.

"You, of course, are the rightful heir to the throne of Iolcos, because Pelias usurped your father Aeson who should now be the rightful king."

"With all due respect, sir," I interrupted. "Are you suggesting that tomorrow I simply leave here, walk down to Iolcos, where I have not been seen for twenty years, stride into the marketplace where all the citizens are assembled and tell them it's my twentieth birthday party as well as their festival, and that I am their rightful king and have come to claim the crown for myself and please will they support me? Have you gone mad?"

"Yes to the first question," replied Cheiron, "and no to the second, and don't be insolent even if you are now almost a fully educated hero. However, you do not qualify fully as a hero until you are judged to be one by your peers, and that will surely follow at some time in the future."

"I'm sorry, sir," I said. "It's just that this is all rather unexpected."

"The unexpected," replied Cheiron, "is exactly what heroes must be prepared for. So tomorrow is a good time to be prepared.

"When you get to the marketplace, you will do as you have suggested. Stride into the marketplace, tell the assembled citizens exactly who you are, explain that it is your twentieth birthday and that you are their rightful king. Pelias will almost certainly be there somewhere, but ignore him if possible. He will get the message and need time to think things over. On no account accept any invitation from him to go back alone with him to his palace, because he will almost certainly kill you. Instead, ask the way to your own father's palace which lies in a small township just over four miles due west of Iolcos. No doubt you will be welcomed by your parents and the palace staff and you can have another birthday party there if you must. Since you will have announced your arrival back home publicly in Iolcos, the news will travel like wildfire throughout Greece and I anticipate that all your father's relations and friends from wherever will come to see you at Aeson's palace. You will get plenty of support and advice on what to do next."

"Is this the start of my great adventure, sir?" I asked.

"It could be," replied Cheiron, "or it could not be. It depends on you. We've taught you nearly all you need to know at this school. Pay respect to the gods and listen to their promptings. You are not the typical hero that leaves our sixth form, but you have qualities which may be exactly what are needed for any adventure you may be involved in. But enough of these platitudes. Tomorrow, get up and get on with it."

"Oh, by the way," he added, "Peleus has agreed to go with you tomorrow. I'm sure you could manage on your own, but he would probably have to join you after a week or so in any case, so he may as well go sooner rather than later. We shall miss him here at the school; good teachers are hard to come by. However, nobody is indispensable.

"And, er, we shall miss you of course," he said as he trotted off to do some more foraging in the forests.

I went to find Peleus, who, I discovered, was not far away.

"Guess what, Peleus?" I said. "Tomorrow is my…"

"I heard," he said. "I was listening to every word. So tomorrow it is, then. And off we go into the big wide world, or something like that. I'm looking forward to it, actually, The last few years have been rather a trial, and an adventure is what we both need, I think.

"So let's get ready. I'll go as I am, but no doubt you will need to sort out suitable clothes and pack your shoulder bag with ample supplies of whatever."

Which is what we did. I was very busy for the rest of the day, checking and double-checking that I had not forgotten to prepare and pack everything that might be needed. I ended up with two shoulder bags, but was sure that Peleus would volunteer to carry one of them.

I then said goodbye to all the staff and fellow students, went to bed and slept like a log.

14

We travel to Iolcos

Next morning, Peleus and I had a very early breakfast, before the rest of the school awoke, and set off north-westwards towards Iolcos. We spent a few minutes at the farm, saying farewell to the farm steward and the few farm-workers, before continuing down the track which meandered along the side of the southern ridge of Mount Pelion and to the west of Mount Pelion itself.

It was spring-time, and the many streams which flowed

down the gullies from the mountain's heights were swollen with melting snow. Crossing them presented no real problem since there were substantial stepping stones at the points where the track crossed them.

But when we came to the River Anaurus, the current was so strong that some of the stepping stones had been swept away. We decided to walk upstream to find a crossing where the water was shallow enough for us to wade across. (We had two staffs each, and they were pointed at one end to act as spears if the need for them should arise. Peleus said that in his experience, it was easy to cross streams with strong currents if you faced downstream using both staffs to steady yourself as you moved sideways across the river.)

We found such a place a few hundred yards upstream and Peleus volunteered to cross first. He used his staff to steady himself against the force of the water, and the depth of the water at its deepest point was only up to his thighs.

"Come on," he shouted when he had gained the opposite bank. "It's easy if you steady yourself with one staff while moving the other. All you need is a strong grip and brawny biceps."

I was just about to wade into the water when I felt a tap on my shoulder. I jumped several feet into the air while turning round at the same time to face the potential adversary. But, when I landed, I was looking into the face of an old hag who stood grinning at me.

"You look like a kind young man," she said, "who would not refuse to help a poor old woman. I need to cross this river, but I'm afraid the current is too strong for my old legs, and I see your companion has crossed easily enough.

If I could cling to your shoulders with my legs round your waist, you should manage it easily, I am sure."

"Of course I will," I replied. "Jump up and we'll be over in about three or four minutes."

I leant forwards and the old woman sprang on to my back with surprising agility. Crossing the river with the extra weight on my back was not easy, but I had had plenty of practice carrying injured sheep on my shoulders across streams almost as difficult as this, and with only one staff to steady me. Farming has its uses.

There was one snag. While I was in mid-stream, one of my sandals stuck firmly between two stones on the riverbed. I twisted my foot this way and that to release it, but to no avail. So I eased my foot out of the sandal and continued without it.

We reached the far bank in about five minutes, and the old woman let herself down from my shoulders. Peleus, when he saw that I was most of the way across and obviously going to make it to his side, walked on down the riverbank towards the track which we had left to find the crossing-place. I turned to say farewell to the old woman, but she was no longer there.

In her place was the goddess Hera.

"Hello again, young Jason," she said. "Still the gallant, I see! Sorry to play a trick on you, but I had to test you to see if you were still the kind of young hero who could achieve divine destiny for that rat Pelias, who still refuses me my customary sacrifices."

"Why does he do that?" I asked.

"Didn't you do mythology at Cheiron's school?" Hera replied. "It's a well-known story."

"I'm sorry," I said. "It's just that I can't remember that particular bit, and there is rather a lot of mythology."

"Well, I'll tell you but I'll keep it brief. Pelias and his brother Neleus were the sons of Tyro and Poseidon. Tyro's parents were the arrogant and ill-fated Salmoneus and his wife Alcidice. Later on Alcidice died and Salmoneus married a hard and difficult woman called Sidero who maltreated Tyro something awful. But that was no excuse for what Pelias did. He hounded Sidero, and when she took refuge at my sanctuary, he violated it by killing her on my very own altars. What do you think of that?"

I was registering suitable disgust and amazement when there was a clap of thunder.

"I'd better be going," said Hera. "When you and your friends see Pelias, and he makes a suggestion on what he thinks you should do, I'll tell you what to say."

There was another clap of thunder and Hera vanished.

"I expect Zeus wants his dinner," I thought to myself, and could not resist a smile.

I heard Peleus shouting, "Come on, Jason. We haven't got all day." I ran to catch him up.

"Where did the old woman go?" he asked.

"Back home to Olympus," I replied, and gave him an account of what had happened.

"The plot thickens," Peleus said, as we walked onwards towards Iolcos. "I suppose you lost your sandal crossing the river. Why don't you abandon the other one, and stop hobbling like that?"

"Because one sandal is better than no sandal," I replied. But although somehow I felt that he was right, I couldn't bring myself to take the other one off, and I could not

69

understand why, especially since going barefoot would have been much more comfortable.

However, we returned to the main track to Iolcos which meandered gradually downhill along the side of mount Pelion and we soon reached the outskirts of Iolcos, which spread south-eastward along the coast.

Most of the inhabitants were obviously gathered in the marketplace some half-mile ahead, to judge from the noise of festivities. But there were still a few farmers, elderly citizens and young children who had declined to go into the city centre and were doing nothing in particular except stare at us as we walked passed them.

"Why do you think they are staring at us like that?" I asked Peleus. "Haven't they seen strangers before?"

"I think it must be the way you look!" he replied.

This surprised me somewhat. I was wearing a normal Magnesian tunic (a kind of extra-long shirt). I noticed that most of those we passed also wore Magnesian tunics, which is not surprising since Iolcos is at the centre of Magnesia (an area of Thessaly which includes Mount Pelion and its ridge to the east and south together with Mount Ossa to its north). But over it I was sporting my favourite leopard-skin jacket. I suppose it must have been that, perhaps with my two spears, which drew their attention, but it was very practical. Light and airy it was, but warm if need be and proof against chilly showers.

"Not to mention your splendid locks of hair which ripple down your back," Peleus continued, grinning like an idiot.

"You can talk," I countered, "with your dirty sheepskin cloak, which incidentally you were wearing on the day I first met you when you butted me into the water-trough."

"I told you it was an accident, and it was," he replied, offended that I had brought the subject up again.

In a few minutes we reached the marketplace. I was hoping that I could have walked unobserved through the crowd, stood on some suitable doorstep, said my piece and gone on my way to my father's palace. It was not to be. The crowd saw us coming and made way for us to pass through. They fell back left and right with looks of amazement and puzzlement on their faces. Eventually we arrived at the place where the sacrifice to Poseidon was obviously going to take place. There were several dozen dignitaries who had apparently been warned of our approach standing facing us as we approached.

One of them opened his mouth to speak to us, but no words came forth. He was staring with what seemed to be great concern at my feet. I noticed that he had a livid scar on his face.

"Young man," he said, "why are you wearing only one sandal?"

I must confess I was not expecting such an irrelevant question. Surely, I thought, any normal person would have asked me who I was and where I had come from and what was I doing there. And why ask me? There were two of us. Why pick on me, just because I had only one sandal?

"All right," he said, "don't tell me if you don't want to. It's enough that you are wearing only one sandal. But tell me this: who are you, where have you come from and what are you doing here?"

That was better. There was almost complete silence as the crowd waited for my reply. I made the speech which I had been preparing all morning:

"My name is Jason. I have spent the first twenty years of my life at Cheiron's School for Heroes, and have been educated by Cheiron, his mother Philyra, his wife Chariclo and his daughter Endeis. I have come home to reclaim my father's ancient kingship of Magnesia which Zeus long ago granted to Aeolus and thereby to his son Cretheus and his son Aeson who is my father. But I am told that one Pelias usurped the kingship from my father, who wisely, as soon as I was born, fearing the violence of the lawless Pelias, secretly sent me away by night, wrapped in purple swaddling clothes as befitted a royal baby, to Cheiron to raise to manhood and kingship. But first I must find my father's palace, so please show me and my companion Peleus the way."

I expected some reply from the assembled dignitaries, but there was none. The man with the scar was about to speak but thought better of it. He turned away and spoke to one of the others, who then approached us, pointed westwards along the seafront and said:

"Aeson's palace is that way. Take my advice and go there straightaway."

We did.

15

We visit my parents' palace

In less than an hour we had arrived at the small township which lay below my father's palace. The inhabitants gathered round us with obvious curiosity, and when we explained who we were and why we had come, they raised a tremendous cheer.

I asked one of them if their town had a name.

"Of course this town has a name," he replied. "We call it Aesonis, after your father Aeson."

Refreshments were immediately provided for us, after which we were carried on their shoulders up the hill to the palace gates.

The clamour had aroused my parents and the palace staff who all came to the entrance hall to meet us. Peleus and I thanked our entourage for their help and hospitality before I turned to embrace my parents.

My parents, Aeson and Alcimede, had tears in their eyes. It was a strange experience for me to meet my parents for the first time. Cheiron and Chariclo had become my substitute parents, and now that I had come face to face with my real parents, I experienced emotions which I find it impossible to describe.

I had been told that they were aged, but to me they looked remarkably young for their years, and I told them so. Aeson confided that he pretended that he was old and decrepit. That way, he explained, Pelias was less likely to worry about him and perhaps try to arrange his funeral. Alcimede said she had always been sure I would return home when I had reached manhood, and the thought of that had kept them both young.

Later that evening, after a sumptuous meal, Aeson, Alcimede, Peleus and I retired to a quiet room with an ample supply of excellent wine, and had a long talk. Of course my parents wanted to know all about my schooling with

Cheiron and Pelias's marriage with Thetis, and this took some time, particularly because Peleus went into considerable detail about the latter.

The conversation then turned to more recent events. I described all that had happened that day, and hoped that Aeson could shed light on some of the things that had puzzled me.

"Have you any idea," I asked Aeson, "who the man with the livid scar was who spoke to me about my missing sandal?"

"Certainly, dear boy," he replied. "That was Pelias himself."

"I thought it might have been," I said. "However, I pretended not to know him. Otherwise I would not have been able to keep my speech brief and get away here."

"Quite right too," Aeson said. "It was a tricky situation, no doubt."

I asked Aeson what was the significance of my missing sandal. He replied that he had heard a rumour that Pelias had been told by an oracle to be 'greatly on guard in every way against a man with one sandal when he comes from the high dwelling-places to the crystal-clear air of the famous land of Iolcos'. "When he saw you," Aeson said, "with a sandal missing on your left foot, he must have remembered the oracle and had a nasty fright, I hope!"

"Do you think Hera had anything to do with me losing the sandal?" I asked him. "Was that all part of some plan for me?".

"Who knows?" replied Aeson. "But it seems somewhat likely, I would have thought!"

"By the way," I asked, "how did Pelias get such a disfiguring scar on his face?"

"That's easy to tell," said Alcimede. "Didn't you do modern mythology at school? Well, before she married Cretheus and produced your father Aeson and his two brothers Pheres and Amythaon…"

"Keep to the point, dear, please," interrupted Aeson.

"…Tyro," continued Alcimede (as though she had not heard him), "had a sordid affair with Poseidon, and produced twins, that rotter Pelias and his dreadful brother Neleus. Tyro kept their birth a secret (and who can blame her?) and abandoned them. They were found by some horse-dealers and one of their mares, perhaps accidentally, kicked Pelias on his face and left that beautiful black-and-blue scar for all to see. That's how it happened!"

Then Aeson asked me what were my plans for the future. It occurred to me that I had none and I told him so.

"Right then," he said, "let me advise you. During the next five days, we shall be entertaining here at my palace many of our relations and supporters who will flock here from many parts of Greece as soon as they hear about what you said in the marketplace at Iolcos earlier today. News like that spreads like wildfire, believe you me!

"On the sixth day, you will go with Peleus and a strong contingent of these relations and supporters to see Pelias. To go alone would be dangerous, but with support you will be able to negotiate from a position of strength. Pelias would not dare try anything treacherous and risk a civil war. You see, he taxes his citizens heavily and gives them little in return; that's why he holds festivals like the one you witnessed yesterday—something to cheer them up and make them think he's not so bad after all. But his citizens have heard that my townsfolk are taxed very lightly and get a lot of public works in return, and I heard that some of them are getting restless, and Pelias knows it. Your arrival and declaration will have given Pelias a lot to worry about."

"But what will I be negotiating *for*?" I asked. "I know I said in Iolcos that I was reclaiming the ancient kingship which Pelias usurped from you, but am I ready yet to take over as king from Pelias, assuming you want me to do that on your behalf? In any case, it strikes me that Pelias is unlikely to yield it without a struggle, although neither of us want to risk a civil war. And another thing, I've had hint after hint from Cheiron and from Hera that I may be on the threshold of some kind of adventure, and I don't call being king of Iolcos my idea of an adventure. Pelias had some time as king of part of Phthia, and he doesn't seem raring to go back to it."

Aeson looked worried. "Shut up for a minute. Didn't Hera give you any advice this morning?" he asked.

I recalled the crossing of the River Anaurus. "Yes," I replied. "She said 'When you and your friends see Pelias, and he makes a suggestion on what he thinks you should do, I'll tell you what to say.'"

"Well, there's your answer!" Aeson said with a smile. "You've nothing to worry about, have you?

"It's very late, and you've had a long day, both of you. Let's go to bed, and let the next six days look after themselves."

So we did, and I didn't sleep very well. I had many dreams in which all the characters and scenes I had met with that day whirled around in fantastic confusion.

16

We encounter Pelias

The next five days were wonderful. My father's palace, though small, was luxurious after Cheiron's cave. The food was rich and varied and there were hills and woods behind the palace where Peleus and I were able to indulge in one of our favourite pastimes—foraging. Aeson also had a small farm and we got some fresh air and exercise as we helped with the lambing.

But what was really exciting was the number of Aeson's relations and friends who from day to day arrived from all over Greece to greet me and wish me well and offer their support.

Most outstanding of the arrivals were Aeson's two brothers who shared his father Cretheus.

The older of the two, Pheres, arrived almost immediately with his wife, Periclymene, from the city of Pherae in Thessaly which he had founded and named after himself. This city was only about ten miles away over the hills, due west of Aeson's palace, and, as Pheres said, so near that if Aeson was ever in real trouble, he could be there to help him in a few hours. He brought thirty-one attendants with him, servants and bodyguards, as well as his two sons Admetus and Lycurgus. Peleus and I immediately took a liking to them. We thought we would teach them some foraging, but, when we did, they showed us a few tricks of their own.

Pheres's younger brother, Amythaon, had married Pheres's daughter Idomene and migrated to Pylos in Messenia in the south-western Peloponnese. This was a three days' journey away, but still they came, bringing with them their two young sons, Melampus and Bias, and twenty-three attendants.

In all, three hundred and seventy-six people came to support us, and this caused quite a domestic problem at the palace. Aeson and Alcimede were determined to act the perfect hosts, and rapidly became overwhelmed in less than half a day. So Periclymene and Idomene took charge and ordered everyone about until there were enough beds and provisions to sleep and feed the whole household. Peleus and I slept in one of the cowsheds, and very clean and comfortable it was too. Not what *you* might expect.

The whole five days were a marvellous family get-together, and we feasted and revelled as never before. Orpheus turned up unexpectedly and his music added magic to the celebrations. I asked him why he had honoured us with his presence. He replied that he liked parties and reminded us of the wedding feast for Peleus and Thetis. Also, he said, he had a feeling that some kind of adventure was brewing and he wanted to be in on it.

Of course these five days of jollity were just what I needed to take my mind off having to go and meet with Pelias on the sixth day, which inevitably arrived after the fifth.

It was decided that the deputation to Iolcos would consist of myself, Peleus as my personal attendant, my two uncles Pheres and Amythaon, and a bodyguard of sixteen warriors from their entourage. We would be accompanied by two hundred other friends, attendants and bodyguards, all well armed, who would surround Pelias's place while we were inside. Aeson said he did not expect foul play but Pelias was never to be trusted.

We sent a messenger early that day to warn Pelias of our approach; otherwise he might have seen our armed party as an attack and started a civil war.

When we arrived, to our surprise, our delegation of twenty was welcomed with great warmth and we were ushered into the presence of Pelias where we were invited to partake of refreshments. We accepted from politeness but I did not relax. Too much was at stake.

"Well, young Jason," said Pelias, "we meet again. When I saw you six days ago on the city seafront, I did not want to respond to your declaration. I was too much surprised and I wanted to think things over. But now I have done so, and would like to hear what you have to say."

I started on my prepared speech.

"O son of Poseidon of the Rock, I greet you. It is important that justice and equity govern our negotiations today. Otherwise we may both regret it. We are both descended through your mother Tyro from her grandfather Aeolus, great ruler of Thessaly, and we are all proud to be called Aeolians. It would be improper therefore for the two of us to dispute our great inheritance with swords and spears. My suggestion is this: you may keep all your wealth in the land of Magnesia, all your fields and sheep and cattle. But I must claim the throne itself which my aged and ailing father Aeson inherited by right from his father Cretheus. I have therefore come to demand your abdication."

"Well spoken, young Jason," Pelias responded. "It shall

be as you wish. I am getting old, while you are in the flower of your youth."

You could have knocked me down with a feather. I had not anticipated this kind of response.

But he continued, "However, there is a problem. I keep getting a dream in which the ghost of Phrixus appears to me and orders me to arrange for his soul to be returned to Iolcos from far-distant Colchis. With his soul he requires that we recover the great Golden Fleece of the ram on which he and his sister Helle were rescued from the knife of their father Athamas."

"I'm sorry," I interrupted, "but it's several years since we did that piece of mythology at school. Could you possibly remind us who Phrixus was and how he and the Golden Fleece ended up so far away?"

"Certainly, dear boy," Pelias replied. "It's important that you know the full story so that you appreciate the significance of Phrixus and the Fleece.

"Athamas was the king of Orchomenos, which you may know is about seventy miles due south from here, at the edge of Lake Copais in Boeotia. He was a son of Aeolus and therefore brother of Salmoneus, my mother Tyro's father. So, in fact, he was the great-uncle of both your father and me. Anyway, his first wife was Nephele and she gave Athamas two children, Phrixus and his sister Helle. For some reason or other that I have forgotten, Nephele disappeared from the scene and Athamas married Ino, one of Cadmus's daughters, and she assumed the part of the wicked stepmother. She had two children of her own by Athamas and she resented the existence of Phrixus and Helle. So she plotted their death.

"She persuaded some women of their country to parch and therefore make sterile the grain which had been set aside for the next sowing. The seed was sown but there were no crops. Athamas sent messengers to seek the advice of the Delphic oracle, but Ino bribed the messengers to report that the oracle advised Athamas that the god required the sacrifice of Phrixus and Helle.

"The children were actually on the altar and Athamas's knife was poised to sacrifice them when Nephele, their real mother, came to the rescue. She sent a golden ram, which could both talk and fly, a gift to her from the god Hermes, which swooped down and told them to jump on to its back. So they flew away across the Aegean sea north-eastward towards the Black Sea. As the ram flew over the straits dividing Europe from Asia, Helle fell off the ram's back and drowned in the sea now known as the Hellespont, named after her.

"The ram flew on and on with Phrixus on its back until it came to the city of Aea, the capital of Colchis at the far eastern end of the Black Sea. Aeetes was, and still is, king of Colchis. He welcomed Phrixus and gave him one of his daughters, Chalciope, in marriage. I believe she presented him eventually with four sons, but I do not know their names. Phrixus sacrificed the ram to Zeus, perhaps on the ram's own instructions, and gave the fleece to King Aeetes, who hung it up in an oak grove, sacred to Ares, and ensured its safety from theft by setting a sleepless serpent to guard over it.

"I have enquired from the oracle at Kastalia what must be done, and I have been told that an expedition by ship must be arranged to recover both the Golden Fleece and the ghost of Phrixus and bring them back to Iolcos. Unless this is done, the anger of those in the underworld will not be appeased and Iolcos will not prosper."

"What has all this got to do with me?" I asked in mock innocence.

"I have been warned by the oracle to beware of a man coming from the country and wearing only one sandal," he replied. "Now what would you do if you were in my shoes, and if you had this problem of having to recover the Golden Fleece?"

I replied without hesitation, "I would send him to fetch the Golden Fleece from King Aeetes, of course.

As soon as I said it, I knew that it was at Hera's prompting, but there was no going back now.

"Good lad," said Pelias. "Accomplish this task for me, and I swear I will hand over to you sole rule and kingship of all Magnesia. May Zeus be our witness."

I supposed that his words signified a binding contract between us, but immediately I asked myself, "Has he tricked me into promising to attempt a seemingly impossible task, fraught with inconceivable dangers and from which I was unlikely to return?"

Clever man, Pelias, I thought, and yet...

17

Aeson arranges all

And then, before I could collect my thoughts, we were all making our way back to my father's palace. The journey seemed to take place in almost complete silence, as though everyone was chewing over in his mind the possible consequences of the meeting with Pelias.

When we arrived back at the palace, I went immediately with Peleus and Aeson's two brothers to report to Aeson in his inner sanctum. In response he said that he would like some time to think the matter over; he then requested that everyone should gather in the main palace courtyard in a few hours' time, when he would deliver his considered opinion on the pact with Pelias and what was to be done about it.

Refreshments were, of course, waiting for us, and, in spite of the tension of the situation, we needed no invitation to enjoy them. After all, it had been a long and stressful morning.

Peleus had spoken little to me on the way back, but while we sat eating our lunch and drinking some excellent wine, he couldn't resist saying something.

"Now that I've had an hour or so to think things over," he said, "I reckon we couldn't have wished for a better outcome. So cheer up, Jason my lad, and I'm sure your father will agree with me."

And then we were all summoned to appear in the main

courtyard, where Aeson was standing on a chair so that we could all see him.

"My friends," he said, "may I take this opportunity of thanking you for coming here to support Jason, my son here, Alcimede my dear wife, and all free-thinking Magnesians who dwell in this palace and in the township around us.

"These have been difficult times for us during the last twenty or so years, while Pelias the unpopular has usurped my kingship and has held the power in Iolcos and Magnesia.

"It may be that you had hoped today that Jason would by now have forced Pelias from his throne and taken over as king. But, really, you cannot have thought such a hope could have been realised without some kind of conflict, even a full-scale civil war. Pelias may be unpopular in Iolcos, but he has a strong following and, with the taxes he has extracted from the populace, he has a loyal bodyguard and police force, not to mention an army of sorts.

"He has, however, made a deal: if Jason here organises an expedition and brings back the Golden Fleece and Phrixus's ghost from Colchis, then he has sworn to hand over the sole rule and kingship of all Magnesia. That is quite a deal.

"Mind you, I dare say he thinks the whole expedition will be a disaster and that even if Jason eventually does somehow get to Colchis, he will never be able to coerce Aeetes into releasing the Fleece from the grip of the sleepless serpent. In other words, he must be thinking that it is impossible that Jason will not meet his death in the attempt, and that he, Pelias, will be able to continue unopposed as king for the rest of his life.

"But he is wrong. Such an expedition is possible and I have reason to believe that it will have the blessing of several gods. All we need is a ship and fifty adventurous men to row it."

Aeson paused while a gasp escaped from his audience followed by a murmur whispering its way round the courtyard.

He continued, "I expect you are thinking that this is all rather wishful thinking, but let me assure you to the contrary. When such a ship is built, and I am assured it can be, how many young men are there here now who would be willing to sail her and row her on an adventure which will be remembered for many thousands of years. Think of the glory of retrieving the Golden Fleece from alien lands and bringing it back to Greece!

"Right then: hands up those who would like to be considered for such an adventure!"

A forest of hands were raised and there was a mighty cheer. I tried to count the hands that were raised but it was impossible. But there were surely over two hundred hands raised from the relations, friends, supporters, servants and bodyguards who were present.

"Thank you, my dear friends," he continued. "I knew the spirit of adventure was alive in you all. But please do not be disappointed if you are not chosen. I believe the number will have to be restricted to about fifty stalwarts, and the privilege will be extended only to those who meet the most stringent tests of character and ability. I propose that Jason's friend Peleus here be appointed recruitment officer and final arbiter of the selection process for the chosen fifty. Peleus, you will know, is destined to be one of the great heroes of Greece, and was in fact granted the extraordinary privilege by the gods of marriage to a goddess. What better man to choose for the job of choosing forty-nine others?

"By the way," he said as an aside to Peleus, "I presume you want to go on the adventure and are willing to act as recruitment officer?"

Peleus was more red in the face than I had seen him for some time, but he stuttered his assent to Aeson: "Of c-c-course, sir. Of c-c-course I will!"

"All those in favour," continued Aeson to the assembled company, "raise their hands!"

"And as for the ship itself," he said without even looking at the forest of hands raised in approval, "I hand you over to our friend Argus here with whom I have just had a brief but serious discussion on the problems of building a ship which will be suitable for such a hazardous journey. He will tell you all about it."

Aeson was helped down from the chair on which he had been standing, and Argus climbed on to it.

18

Argus describes the Argo

Argus was a man of average build but with huge and powerful hands. He had a belt round his waist into which were slotted tools of various sorts, with pride of place being given to a wicked looking little adze which I discovered later was his favourite tool.

He cleared his throat, wiped his brow and began to speak:

"My friends, please excuse me wearing my tool belt but I never like to be without it. Tools are expensive and I once had all my favourite tools stolen from my workshop at the shipyard. Perhaps I should explain for the benefit of those who do not know me that I am a master shipwright and come from a long line of master shipwrights who have been building boats, mainly for fishermen, but also of late for merchants and traders who are getting more and more adventurous as regards the distances they are prepared to row and sail in order to get rich. Some of them tell me they have now explored beyond the Aegean into the straits between Europe and Asia where the currents are very strong and as a result they are demanding larger boats with larger sails and more and more oars. It is hard to keep up with the technology, but I am assisted always, as indeed were my forbears, by our great patron goddess Athena who guides my hands and inspires my calculations.

"So I regard the building of the ship which will recover the Golden Fleece as a challenge which will be the next stage in the development of shipbuilding technology. It will certainly need to be the largest and most powerful boat ever built up to this time. I have already completed some quick specifications and these are as follows:

"The craft will have one large central sail. There will be fifty oars but in normal travel only forty will be in use. This will mean that, of fifty oarsmen, ten can be taking one period of rest in five, during which they can be assigned maintenance and galley duties as the need arises. However, in the event of strong currents, all fifty oarsmen will be available to power the vessel at the discretion of the skipper. Overall, I suggest that there be a crew of fifty-four, consisting of skipper, helmsman and fifty-two oarsmen, the extra two over the fifty being to allow for accidents and fatalities.

"The material to be used for the hull and all main parts will be best quality Pelion pine. I shall require a team of volunteers to cut the timber and mules to drag it from the forest to the shipyard. Of course only I shall be responsible for selecting the trees to be felled.

"My shipyard is, as most of you know, about five miles east-south-east from here, at Pagasae, on the southern side of the bay and opposite Iolcos. Fortunately it is nearly a three-mile walk round the bay from Iolcos to my shipyard which will give some degree of privacy from the eyes of Pelias and his gang. I shall need twenty volunteers to help me build the boat, and those of you who are not used to hard work and following orders and instructions without question need not apply. If you wish to be considered, simply follow me down to the yard when I leave. Remember: most of you are unlikely to be picked to sail in her, but to have taken part in her creation will endow you with a glorious reputation.

"Any questions?"

Argus almost immediately got down from the chair on which he had been standing, but there were some questions, and he had to get back up again.

"How long will it be?" asked Pheres's son, Admetus.

"About ninety-eight feet overall," answered Argus. "Any other questions?"

"Sorry, sir" said Admetus. "I meant how long will it take to build, in terms of days?"

"Then why," responded Argus, "didn't you ask me that in the first place? Forty days, give or take a few, depending on the weather and whether the volunteers are up to scratch or not. That will take us to mid-spring, which leaves five or six lunar months before the winter weather makes voyaging inadvisable."

"What about a name for her?" asked Aeson.

"I don't name my ships," replied Argus. "Why don't we leave it to Jason? It's his expedition."

Everyone turned to look as me. I had already been thinking of a suitable name, and I replied without delay.

"We must call her **_ARGO_**," I said, "because 'argos' means 'swift' and because Argus here will have built her."

"Two good reasons," said Aeson. "So '_Argo_' it will be."

Argus, seemingly pleased, nodded in agreement, descended from the chair and without another word left to go to his shipyard. He was followed by fifty-seven potential volunteers, of whom, no doubt, only twenty would be chosen.

"A man after my own heart, that Argus," I remarked to Peleus later, when the meeting had dissolved. "No vagueness with _his_ numeracy, I hope you noticed."

"Er…yes," he replied. "But where do you think I'm going to get fifty-odd heroes from in forty days to go on this crazy adventure of yours?"

"It's fifty-four including you and me, so get that right from the start," I replied with a laugh. "However, that's your problem."

"But less of a problem than Thetis was," he replied. "I

expect I'll cope! Let's go and do a bit of foraging in the woods behind here. We need to relax after all today's efforts."

And so we did.

19

Preparations for the voyage

Surprisingly, Peleus got on with the job of recruiting the crew for the *Argo* with some degree of efficiency. To start with, he did not attempt to do it on his own, despite the fact that in his travels he had gained all kind of contacts. He approached Aeson and his two brothers, and together they drew up a list of potential adventurers.

They then sent out heralds throughout Greece, mainly to Thessaly, Aetolia, Boeotia, the Peloponnese, and across the Aegean sea to Miletus, with suitable invitations. None of those invited refused; in fact so keen was the response that they came almost immediately to Aeson's palace to stay until the *Argo* was built and ready to sail.

This caused a number of accommodation problems, but Alcimede and Aeson solved them with their usual efficiency. I was glad to have the opportunity to get to know them before the voyage, and the fact that they did not all arrive at the same time helped considerably.

I suspect that some of you may be worried that I shall, at this point, give a list of all the Argonauts, together with details of their home city, parentage and other titbits like that. I must confess that I was on the point of so doing when it occurred to me that you might find that more than a little boring, like asking you to read one of your telephone books. So what I have done is make such a list with what I hope are some interesting titbits where appropriate, and I have placed it at the end of this book in a glossary. Some of the Argonauts did not play a prominent part in the adventure, and so, poor souls, their only mention will be in that glossary, which is your good fortune, if not theirs.

But some of the Argonauts do deserve a mention at this point, because they did play a major part in the expedition. So I trust that you will allow me a few words about them.

There was **Orpheus**, of course, who had turned up soon after we arrived in Iolcos. I was glad he was keen to join the expedition because his music would cheer the crew and calm the sea.

And, guess who! **Heracles** himself, the strongest man in the world, ever, and that includes Samson whose strength is recorded in what you call the Old Testament. When he heard about our proposed expedition he was carrying a live boar on his back as part of one of his labours. He immediately dropped it, tied it up, left it at the entrance to the market at Mycenae and hotfooted it to join us.

A few of the Argonauts were able to perform unusual feats. The twin sons of Boreas, the North Wind were an example. Their names were **Zetes** and **Calais**. They could fly! They had dark wings, sparkling with golden scales fluttering from their temples and their feet. When they flew, their long hair streamed in the wind over their shoulders and down their backs, a sight which always filled me with wonder. This ability to fly came in useful on the expedition.

Three other geniuses are worth mentioning. There was **Euphemus** of Taenarum, son of Poseidon; his father gave him the ability to walk on water, and he could run so swiftly over water that he did not get his feet wet—only the tips of his toes sank in the water. **Periclymenus**, a grandson of Poseidon, had boundless strength and the ability to change himself into any form he might want. **Idmon** was a son of Apollo and his divine parentage endowed him with the art of prophesy, through the observation of the behaviour of birds and the signs in burnt offerings; his predictions were important to us.

You may already have heard of **Castor** and Pollux, the heavenly twins. Pollux was originally known as **Polydeuces**. They were young at the time of the expedition. These twins were the sons of Leda and either her husband Tyndareus (a Lacedaemonian or Spartan hero) or Zeus himself (masquerading as a swan), both of whom slept with Leda during the same night. They were borne by Leda at the same time as another pair of twins, Helen and Clytemnestra, both of whom caused a lot of trouble later on. Their curious parentage gave me the opportunity to ask Castor and Polydeuces questions like "How's your dad?" which invariably elicited a ribald response. The skill of Polydeuces as a boxer came in useful on the expedition, but Castor's skill with horses was not much use, though he was a brave warrior.

A tenth Argonaut was **Iphitus** the son of Naubolus. There was another Argonaut named Iphitus, the son of Eurytus, who inherited a great bow from his father. Many years later, after our adventures, he gave it to Odysseus, who used it to slay the suitors of his wife Penelope; but that is another story which you may already know. However, this Iphitus, the son of Naubolus, was king of Phocis. When Peleus had done all he could towards his recruiting exercise, on the tenth day of the forty needed to build the *Argo*, my father suggested we go to consult the oracle at Delphi concerning our proposed expedition, and it was Iphitus who entertained Peleus and me most royally in his palace when we went there. We travelled on the two magnificent horses, Balius and Xanthus, which Poseidon (you may remember) had given to Peleus and Thetis as a wedding gift and were stabled at my farm at Cheiron's school. Our journey to Delphi on those magnificent steeds was exhilarating. And as for Delphi—phew! Perched on the southern side of mount Parnassus in Phocis, the site of the oracle was awe-inspiring. Iphitus came with us to the sanctuary where the oracle spoke to us through his sacred laurel tree, and his utterances (unintelligible to us) were interpreted for us by his priests. Apollo promised to "signal the fulfilment and goal of our voyage". We took this to mean that our expedition would be successful, and Iphitus immediately insisted on joining us.

The names of these ten and forty-two other Argonauts were inscribed by a palace servant on a pillar in the main hall of Aeson's palace. When I looked at the list, I discovered that Peleus's name was not included in the list. I asked him who had prepared the list.

"I did, of course," he said. "I dictated it to the scribe."

"Then where is your name?" I asked him.

He looked up and down the list several times, and turned red.

"Oh dear," he said, "I keep forgetting to count myself. However, I'm sure the list is right, and if you add my name, you'll see there are fifty-two names."

"I am sorry to correct you," I said, "but that would make fifty-three, not fifty-two. So we are still one short of the fifty-four as recommended by Argus."

"But," replied Peleus, "there are two surprise Argonauts whose names are not on the list yet. They did not want their names to appear until the start of the voyage, for private and security reasons."

"Who are they?" I asked him.

"Not going to tell you," said Peleus. "I'm keeping it as a surprise for the actual day."

"Be like that if you want," I said. "But it still remains that we have fifty-five, one too many, if we add your name and the names of your mysterious two to this list here."

Peleus was silent for a minute or two. Then he said, "Well, does it matter?" and walked off.

I tried asking Aeson and his brothers about the two whose names were not on the list, but did not get anywhere. And so, for the rest of the time before we set sail, I was kept wondering who they were.

A few days later Peleus could not help asking me if I had guessed who the two mysterious Argonauts were. And I could not help replying, "Well, does it matter?"

To which Peleus responded, "Probably," and walked off again.

Sometimes he irritates me, does Peleus, but I was glad he was going to be one of the crew.

But I am neglecting to tell you about the building of

the *Argo* which was taking place while the Argonauts were assembling at the palace.

20

The Building of the Argo

The boatyard of Argus was at Pagasae, on the opposite side of the bay from Iolcos, and Argus and his "volunteers" started to work on the *Argo* immediately they arrived there from the meeting at the palace. It was going to be the largest and most ambitious vessel up to that time. The confidence with which Argus set about the task was startling until I remembered that it was Athena herself who was his patron and who guided his hands and inspired his calculations.

I walked down there from the palace most days, intrigued to see how a boat of such a size was to be built.

The first time Peleus and I went down to the yard with a few Argonauts from the early arrivals, we were met with rather a gruff reception from Argus.

"What do you lot want?" he asked without looking up from a plank he was shaping. "If you are all going to come down here every day getting in the way, we may as well postpone the trip till next year or the one after."

"Sorry," I replied, "but we cannot but help being interested since we are going to sail in her. But I'll tell you what. Suppose we promise that only Peleus and I will in future come into the yard, just to look, and perhaps talk briefly to you, provided you are not too busy, and all the others observe from that high ground over there outside the yard. Would that be acceptable to you?"

"I suppose so," Argus grunted, "but talk only to me. I've enough trouble getting these twenty idle layabouts to do precisely what I tell them without them being distracted by a lot of silly questions."

"Well, yes," I replied, "but they do seem to be getting on with their work, and they are only volunteers."

"Volunteers be damned," replied Argus. "When I picked this twenty from the fifty-seven volunteers, I made it quite clear to them all that any more than twenty would be tripping over each other, that they were privileged to be chosen and that they would only be able to boast of their part in building the most famous ship of all time if they obeyed my orders, put their backs into their work and stayed the course."

"Not that way, you fool," he said, turning aside to speak to one of the twenty, who was chiselling a mortise into the edge of one of the planks. "Look—like this. How many more times must I tell you?"

And we presumed correctly that we were dismissed.

On subsequent visits, Peleus and I confined ourselves in the main to observing rather than asking questions, and Argus learnt to ignore us, or at least not to object to our presence.

Of course, I was a complete novice as far as boat-building was concerned. Peleus knew a little about it, and was able to explain some of the technicalities to me. It was not until well over half of the forty days had passed that the *Argo* had reached the stage of building where we were able to envisage what the completed vessel would look like. After that point, we became even more excited to see her completed.

Perhaps now is the time to give you a brief description of her main features and dimensions.

Argo, as Argus had specified, was (to the nearest foot) ninety-eight feet long overall. At her fattest width she was ten feet wide. Her keel was straight but curved up slightly at the front to meet the rear of her "snout" or "ram" or "cutwater" which curved down forwards from her prow (or maybe you call it bow nowadays) down to sea level. This snout was one of her more unusual features and Argus said it would cut through the water like a knife, and flatten the bow wave to make the water smoother for the oarsmen. There was a large knob on the tip of the snout and a series of five broad pegs at one-foot intervals up the front of it stopping at foredeck level.

"What on earth are those steps up the front of the boat for?" I asked Argus.

Argus sighed and replied, "They are the prow boarding-steps, and you can use them as hand-holds and foot-holds for boarding. When *Argo* is in the water, the ram is a convenient point for swimmers to gain access to vessel."

"In addition," Argus added, after a few moments for thought, "the ram makes a very convenient toilet with automatic flushing whenever the vessel is moving."

I detected a slight twinkle in Argus's eye as he provided this information, but I could not be sure.

And then Argus showed me something amazing.

"Look up there," he said, pointing to the foremost point of the prow. At the top of the cutwater, joining the handrails of the foredeck together, was an oak beam, rising vertically from deck level to about twelve inches above the handrail and carved to resemble the goddess Athena.

"That beam," he continued, "was provided by the goddess Athena. It is made from a bough cut from the sacred oak which grows in the sanctuary of Zeus at Dodona in Epirus. One night, when we were all asleep, Athena herself fitted it to the stem where you now see it. It can speak!"

I looked carefully at Argus to see if he was joking, but his expression was serious.

"Have you heard it say anything yet?" I asked him.

"No," he replied.

Both the foredeck at the prow and the quarterdeck at the stern provided ample decking for those of the crew who were not rowing. There was a good space under each for storage and cooking and protection from the elements for some of the crew.

The rear of the keel curved up under the stern and continued in a graceful arc upwards and backwards and then forwards over the quarterdeck, ending in a snail-like decoration. I asked Argus why this was, and he replied that all proper boats ended up like that at the stern.

The main body of the *Argo*, between the foredeck and quarterdeck contained twenty-five rowing benches each of which spanned the whole width of the boat and was spaced at three-foot intervals. A wide gangway went centrally down the whole length, and the mast was situated about one-third of the way down it from the prow. When it was not raised for sailing the mast and the furled sail were stowed down the length of the gangway, and the partly unfurled canvas of the sail, in this position, could provide some degree of protection in the event of inclement weather.

In between each bench on the side of the vessel were stout thole-pin blocks, on the pins of which the oars swivelled. Each oar was counterweighted at the hand end to make the oar balanced and therefore lighter to handle. Also, when the oars were not in use, each one could be lifted off the thole-pin and its handle moved as far as possible across the boat to the side of the oarsman opposite, thereby raising the oar-blade as far as possible from the battering of the waves.

The *Argo* was steered by the helmsman standing on the quarterdeck. He operated two angled steering oars, one port, one starboard, each pivoted at a point on the side-rail towards the front of the quarterdeck.

The sail, when hoisted, was controlled by ropes for the ends of which Argus had provided belaying pins on a stout beam at waist height across the front of the quarterdeck.

I was puzzled by what the volunteer had been doing when Argus reprimanded him for his technique while chiselling a mortise in a plank edge. Peleus decided to risk it and ask Argus what it was for.

"Surely," Peleus asked him, "a hole like that will weaken the plank, or has it a purpose?"

There was an ominous silence as Argus ceased working with his adze, changed colour from sunburnt sienna to apoplectic purple, and then slowly back again to sienna.

"The planks are *not* weakened," said Argus, "by being joined together by mortise and tenon joints. They are strengthened by synergy. Each joint consists of a small mortise, or pocket-like slot in the plank-edge, with a corresponding mortise in the plank-edge adjacent to it. A tenon, or small tongue of wood, sits tightly, half in one mortise and half in the other. To secure the tenon in the mortises, two small holes are bored through the outside of the plank into each end of the tenon, and two wooden plugs are driven tightly into each hole, thereby locking the tenon securely into the mortises and ensuring that the planks are firmly fixed together.

"Have you understood what I have been saying? I have tried to explain the holes in the boat to you as simply as possible, but if you still feel that the galley is unsafe, you can test the strength of the joints by trying to pull this plank here away from the one beneath it. Please feel free to try. I shall not mind. I do so want you all to feel confidence in the *Argo*. After all, your lives will depend on her not falling apart when she is put under stress."

Argus paused, and stared hard at Peleus, whose colour had turned somewhat red.

"Thank you very much," he responded coolly, "for your very clear and concise explanation of a technical matter which had been puzzling me. My knowledge of ship-building, though less than elementary, has, I feel, now been increased considerably, and I feel that I shall now be able to explain these tortoises and melons to my future shipmates, thereby saving you the tedium of having to repeat your excellent explanation."

Argus seemed satisfied, even somewhat amused and flattered by Peleus's response. No more was said. Argus returned to his work and Peleus and I walked away to join our companions who were watching from the high ground outside the shipyard.

"What are they chiselling all those little holes into the edges of the planks for?" asked Telamon, Peleus's brother.

Peleus smiled broadly. As he began his explanation, I decided that enough was enough. It was time for me to walk home alone to Father's palace for supper.

On the thirty-ninth day of the building of the *Argo*, we went down yet again to see Argus. I asked him how near she was to completion.

"I said forty days," he said, "and I meant forty days. She'll be ready to launch first thing tomorrow, and," he added, turning to look at the twenty volunteers who were scurrying about like bluebottles, "in spite of everything this lot has done, or rather, not done, to delay the completion of the project.

"However…" he continued.

"Stop work for one minute, please," he shouted to the volunteers, "and gather round here."

They did so, and he addressed the assembled company:

"By midnight, provided you keep at it and don't slack off your efforts, *Argo* will be complete and ready for launching. I want her ship-shape and Pagasae-fashion, or I'll know the reason why. If you want to celebrate the completion, please do so after midnight and before dawn. You can borrow the torches you use for working the night-shifts, but make sure you return them to the shed in good condition, primed with fresh oil. Tomorrow the Argonauts themselves will launch the *Argo*, under my instructions, and you may watch from the high ground over there.

"And…thank you for helping me finish the building of the *Argo* on time and with a degree of craftsmanship of which you can all justifiably be proud."

The twenty returned to their work and I noticed great grins of satisfaction on their faces.

"Thank you, Argus," I said to him.

"Yes, well, I've still a bit more to do, if you will excuse me," he replied, and that was that.

21

We walk to Pagasae

Next morning excitement was at fever-pitch at Aeson's palace. It was the day when *Argo* would be launched ready for sailing on the following day.

We were all up at crack of dawn. My father left his bedroom to behold his courtyard seething with fifty-three budding Argonauts—heroes, kings, demi-gods—all of them fussing around checking their armour and the rest of their gear.

"I'll say goodbye to you later," he said to me. "With all this racket going on, I think I shall go back to bed for a while."

My mother, on the other hand, was fussing round them all, giving their armour a final polish or folding their spare clothes more neatly into their shoulder bags.

It had been decided that all of them, except for Peleus and me, would process down from Aesonis to the *Argo* in the boatyard at Pagasae soon after breakfast, in order to give me some quiet and privacy with my parents before I too left to join them at the coast. Peleus said he would stay behind to accompany me because he thought the townsfolk would probably be lining the path down to the sea, and I would look silly walking down on my own.

We waved to the other fifty-one Argonauts as they left the palace gates to process through the town. As expected, the road was thronged with the townsfolk of Aesonis who cheered them on their way.

The morning was clear and bright but with a cool breeze, and the sun glinted on their armour as the Argonauts swaggered along. It was a magnificent sight, a procession of nearly all of the most outstanding men of all Hellas, gathered together for an adventure which had never been attempted before and the like of which would never be attempted again.

As I saw them disappearing round a bend in the road, I overheard the following snatches of conversation:

"What on earth was Pelias thinking of, getting so many famous noblemen together for an expedition which will deprive the whole of Hellas of their valour?...I bet if Aeetes refuses to give them the Golden Fleece of his own free will, such a band of warriors could burn his palace to the ground the moment they get there... . But they've got to get there first, and that won't be easy, I can tell you...I feel sorry really for Aeson, so old and fragile, and, by all accounts, not likely to live to see his son return, always assuming he does return...I feel more sorry for poor Alcimede, getting her son back after all these years, and now losing him again so soon... . It's a great pity that when Helle fell into the Hellespont, Phrixus and the ram didn't fall in as well; it would have saved all this grief... . Do you know, that wretched ram actually *chatted* to Phrixus when Helle fell off, can you believe it?...I'm so glad I didn't miss the procession; there's not much going on in Aesonis these days, is there? …"

I could not help smiling. If Aeson's pretence of senility and ill-health could fool even the townsfolk of Aesonis on his doorstep, it was very unlikely that Pelias would attempt anything nasty against him while we were away.

Peleus and I went back into the palace. I bandaged up Peleus's ankle (there had been a pot-hole in the pavement where we had been standing) and left him to finish his packing (such as it was) while I went into my parents' bedroom to say my farewells.

"I must say," said Aeson, "I shall be glad to have a bit of peace and quiet after the last forty days, though it was an experience I would not have missed for anything. The oracle was encouraging, and I know enough about you now to know you can look after yourself. There will be dangers, but you will be in the company of over fifty of the finest and bravest men of all Hellas. In any case, I believe that Peleus will prove to be an outstanding friend, and I've told him to keep his eye on you, because you may meet some strange women on your journey, and, if you will excuse me saying so, you have not had much practice in coping with them as yet."

"I'm sure any boy of mine," interrupted Alcimede, "is quite capable of coping with women, don't you worry about that."

"I'm not worried," continued Aeson. "Just concerned. However, time will tell."

"Don't you worry about me," I said. "The oracle was favourable, and I daresay our unique range of skills will be a match for any opposition we may encounter. It's you two who have to be careful while I am away. The danger will be if, after we have been away a while, a false rumour circulates that we have been lost. If Pelias suspects that we will not return, he may decide to tidy things up by arranging your death, dear Father, especially since many of your supporters will be away with me on the *Argo*. So keep a low profile, as you have been doing.

"As for you, Mother dear, I think it would be a good idea if you came with me to the gates of the palace, where you can be seen by the crowd, and give a display of grief at my departure. I think I saw two of Pelias's spies mingling with the crowd, and they will, no doubt, be reporting everything back to him as soon as we embark. Aeson's non-appearance will indicate his illness and your distress will give the impression that you do not expect ever to see me again."

"Agreed," said Alcimede, and they both embraced me and wished me good luck.

I called upon Peleus to carry my gear, and he accompanied Alcimede and me to the palace gates. The crowd were still there, expectantly lining the main street down through Aesonis. As expected, the two spies of Pelias were there, as near as they could get to the gates without calling attention to the fact that they were strangers to the town.

Mother immediately started her speech:

"Oh Jason, Jason. If only I had died on that dreadful day when Pelias tricked you into this dangerous adventure. Then you could have buried me in my grave with your own two hands. You've been a good boy to me, repaying all my love for you, and burying me was all I would have asked of you. As it is, you leave me all alone in this empty palace, pining away with love for you, my only son. When I learned of the story of Phrixus and Helle and the golden ram, never did I think that they would bring me so much grief. Oh woe is me! Woe! Woe!"

As she grasped me suffocatingly to her breast, I whispered in her ear, "That's enough, dear. Don't overdo it. My turn now."

"Mother dear," I said, "your tears will not save me from misfortune. The gods control our future, and we must both take what comes with courage. The voyage will, no doubt, be threatened with great dangers, but Athena has helped us build our boat and will be with us, Phoebus Apollo has given us favourable oracles, and remember the nobility and courage of our crew. So cease your tears and do not be a bird of ill-omen to the *Argo*. Return into the palace. You will not be alone. You have your ladies-in-waiting, and Aeson, though very frail, is still with you. Wish me luck as you wave me goodbye."

And off I went, with Peleus following. We were not alone, because a few of the palace servants, bless them, insisted on accompanying us. The crowd who had been waiting for us in Aesonis cheered us on our way, and even on the path from the town to the sea there were farmers and their families who patted our backs and wished us well.

22

We launch the Argo

Our friends, the Argonauts, were waiting for us on the beach by the boatyard, and waved their hands in welcome as we joined them.

"I have just done a quick count," I remarked to Peleus, "and their are fifty-three of us here, including you and me. What about the other two?"

Peleus smiled. "One is already here," he said. "In fact he's standing right behind you."

I turned, expecting at least a demi-god or a son of a goddess. Argus the ship-builder was standing there, with what I took to be a grin on his face. Over his shoulders he had thrown a cloak made from the shaggy hide of a black bull; it stretched right down to his feet. He was obviously expecting to go somewhere. He spoke:

"If you think I am going to let you lot sail in my masterpiece without me being present to ensure that you sail her correctly and within her limits of endurance, you are mistaken. In any case, she could occasionally be in need of minor repairs, as a result of mishandling, and you will need my advice and expertise in that respect. I shall ask for no reward for my free consultancy, but I shall expect you to give it your unquestioning attention."

"Thank you for your polite consideration," I replied. "We shall welcome you aboard. You will, of course be expected to take your turn at the oars with the others, and I have no doubt that, if we are engaged in battle on our journey, you will acquit yourself well."

Argus looked closely into my eyes until I nearly blinked. "Have no worries on that score, young Jason," he said. He turned and walked away.

"Got you there," said Peleus. "And here comes the last Argonaut, walking along the shore over there."

I shielded my eyes from the sun, and there, approaching us from Iolcos, was Acastus, son of Pelias. I recognised him from our meeting with Pelias six days after our arrival at my father's palace.

"What on earth is he doing here?" I asked Peleus. "Surely he supports his own father?"

"Apparently not," he replied. "It is not unknown for princes to rebel against their father's opinions and policies, especially when their regime is oppressive to all and sundry. He came to see me soon after our meeting with Pelias. He said he was disgusted with his father's power-mania, and he thought it would teach him a lesson if he, Acastus, his father's only son, joined the expedition which his father had conceived. In any case, he wanted to come. He was fed up with a life of indolence at the palace, and looked forward to some action."

By the time Peleus had finished speaking, Acastus had arrived and immediately walked up to me. He was wearing a brilliant double-folded cloak.

"Please may I join your expedition?" he asked. "No doubt Peleus here has told you my reasons for disobeying my father. If you are interested, the cloak which I see you are admiring was made for me by my sister, Pelopeia. Perhaps she will make one for you when we get back!"

"I shall be glad to have you on board," I replied. "You'll need your cloak to keep you warm at nights, and there will be ample room for you to stow it under your rowing-bench."

As Acastus joined the others, I climbed up on to a convenient boulder and told the assembled Argonauts to find seats on *Argo*'s mast and furled sail which were still lying on the beach.

They took some time doing this, some positions apparently being better than others, but eventually they sorted themselves out, and I addressed them:

"Friends," I said, "*Argo* is ready for us. Thanks to the skill of Argus here, who is, of course, joining our expedition, our ship is the largest and finest ever built. Moreover the oracle which I consulted at Delphi has promised to guide us safely through to our journey's end.

"But before we start, we must decide who is to be the captain of *Argo* and the leader of you, the Argonauts. I suggest you choose not only the bravest of our band, but also someone who will take full responsibility for the adventure, someone with the ability to settle any differences which may arise between us and to negotiate with the many foreigners whom we shall no doubt encounter."

It was obvious to me that I would have to be both captain and leader, since the whole expedition was my responsibility. However, I considered that my position should be clear and definite right from the start, and desired the wholehearted approval of the crew to be established with certainty by a show of hands.

With one voice the Argonauts shouted for Heracles to be their leader. This took me rather by surprise, to put it mildly. I knew he was the strongest man in the world, but did that make him the ideal choice? Somewhat disconcerted, I asked for a show of hands.

The vote was unanimous. But Heracles without hesitation stood up and shouted (he had a commanding voice as well as a commanding stature):

"No, no, no, no, no! I am not your man. Yes, Jason must lead us. He is the hero who has brought us together here, and it is he, and no other, who must be our leader and the captain of the *Argo*."

And immediately the Argonauts cheered and shouted, "Jason for leader! Speech! Speech! Speech!"

"Thank you," I replied, "for your confidence in me. Right! We must get on with it and waste no more time. Now pay attention!

"Before we sail, we must appease Phoebus Apollo with a sacrifice, and we shall combine doing so with a feast. We shall need two oxen, and I have already sent two of the palace servants to fetch them from my farm back at Cheiron's School for Heroes. They should be here with them very soon.

"In the meantime, we must launch the *Argo* into the water, get all the tackle on board and cast lots for your places on the rowing-benches.

"Thirdly, we must build an altar on the beach, ready for our sacrifice to Apollo."

"That," muttered Peleus, "should have been 'fourthly' if you want accuracy."

"Apollo," I continued, ignoring him, "as you surely know, is the god of embarkation. He promised me, when I consulted him, that he would reward our sacrifice to him by revealing to me the sea-lanes of our voyage."

110

"Right then," I said. "Firstly let us launch the *Argo*! Obviously we shall all get wet, so I suggest you pile up all your clothes on that high slab of rock over there."

Which they did, and then, under the command of Argus, we threw a stout rope right round and under the *Argo*, and twisted it tight on each side. The idea of this, Argus pointed out, was to give additional strength to the hull particularly during launching but also during the voyage when the pounding of the seas would put considerable strain on the mortise and tenon joints which held the planks together.

Next, we were instructed to hollow out a slipway running from the prow of *Argo* down into the sea, which we then fitted with polished timber rollers for the hull to glide on. The fifty oars were then raised onto the galley with their blades inside her and the handles projecting eighteen inches out from the thole pins to which we lashed them. Fifty of us then positioned ourselves between the oars on each side of the galley.

I had already chosen one of the Argonauts to be helmsman. He was Tiphys, who came from Siphae, a town on the southern coast of Boeotia. I had been told that he was an expert mariner who was able to sense a swell coming across the sea, could feel the onset of storms and could use the sun or stars to navigate. What better man could there have been to steer our galley?

Tiphys, without any prompting from me, leapt on board. We gripped and breasted the oar handles, and when Tiphys gave the command to push, we strained with our legs until *Argo* began to leave her supports and glided onto the rollers. Dark smoke arose as the keel chafed the slipway, but such was the skill of Argus's preparations and Tiphys's commands for us to heave together that *Argo* swiftly slid down into the sea where we held her in check by her hawsers.

We then reversed the oars, fitting them to the thole pins, stowed the mast and sail on board down the central gangway and packed all our stores for the voyage away tidily under the foredeck and the quarterdeck, carefully protected by oilskins.

Back on the beach, I organised a lottery by which the Argonauts were allocated to rowing-benches; I thought this a better arrangement than leaving it to each individual to choose his own position since that would surely have led to frequent arguments. No regular positions were allocated to five of us: Tiphys the helmsman, Zetes and Calais (whose wings would have made rowing difficult except in an emergency), Orpheus who was needed to calm the waves and the sailors with his music, and, of course, myself who, as captain, would be required to be available at all times for policy-making and decisions. In addition, I assigned Heracles and Ancaeus to the central bench (which Argus, at my request, had made especially strong for them) because of their great size. (Ancaeus came from Arcadia and was an outsize Argonaut who came dressed in a bearskin from a bear he caught on Mount Maenalus and brandishing a huge two-edged axe in his right hand.) The other forty-eight had to accept their positions from the lottery. There was a certain amount of grumbling when some of them learnt of their rowing partner. But most of them seemed quite happy, since I had arranged the lottery so that brothers and friends were placed near each other.

"You fixed that lottery," Peleus whispered to me, "didn't you?"

"To a certain extent," I replied, "but I never said it would be random, did I?"

"Well," he continued, "why don't you get us to stow our personal effects under our benches, now that you have fiddled them for us?"

"What a good idea," I replied. "What would I do without you?"

And so, at my suggestion, the Argonauts carefully stowed away their own treasured possessions, with the exception of Peleus, who didn't seem to have any.

"Haven't you got anything to stow away?" I asked him.

"What's the point when you always seem to have anything I might need?" he replied.

At which point the stewards arrived on the beach leading two magnificent oxen from my farm.

23

A lot of feast and a little fuss

We piled up shingle from the beach and fashioned an altar to Apollo. On top we spread logs of dried olive-wood which servants had brought down from the palace. Some of the younger Argonauts kept the oxen under control while others prepared lustral water for sprinkling over the participants and barley-grains for scattering over the victims and the altar.

I asked for silence and prayed aloud:

"Lord Apollo, you who dwell in Iolcos and Aesonis, which bears my father's name, and didst promise to guide us safely through to our journey's end, we pray you to be mindful of your promise. So we, in turn, promise on our return to sacrifice to you on your altar as many bulls in number as we who shall return to this shore, and countless other brilliant offerings. Receive then this sacrifice here as we prepare to embark. Prosper, we beseech you, our voyage with calm seas and gentle breezes. Amen."

And then I scattered the barley-grains over the altar and the oxen.

I was expecting Peleus to make some caustic comment about my choice of words, but his look was solemn, and I was glad that he appeared to show reverence for the occasion.

When he did speak, he mumbled to me, "Well done, Jason. I'm glad it was you who spoke the prayer. I think I would probably have been tongue-tied."

And so we proceeded with the sacrifice. Heracles stunned the first ox with his club and Ancaeus the second with his bronze axe. Others then slaughtered the beasts and flayed the hides. They removed the thigh-pieces which they covered carefully with fat and burnt them on spits. Meanwhile I poured out libations of pure wine. Bright flames arose all round the sacrifice and dark smoke spiralled upwards into the sky.

One of the Argonauts was Idmon, who was a son of Apollo, though his mortal father was Abas, the son of Melampus, son of my uncle Amythaon. His divine parentage endowed him with the art of prophesy, through the observation of the behaviour of birds and signs in burnt offerings. He had been watching the sacrifice intently and now came forward to speak:

"My friends, those of you who are used to watching sacrifices will no doubt be aware that what we have just seen is most propitious. The signs are that the expedition will be a success despite many trials on the way."

This announcement was greeted with a heart-warming cheer from all those around him. But Idmon continued:

"However, I myself am fated to die on the journey, far off in the mainland of Asia, and this I have known for some time now from observing the flight of birds. Nevertheless, come with you I must. I wish my family to be proud of me."

There was silence. We were all sad to learn that Idmon would never return to these shores. Peleus broke the silence:

"We are all very grateful to you, dear Idmon, for interpreting the signs of our sacrifice, and are glad to learn that the expedition will succeed. Yes, there will doubtless be many trials on the way, and your death will deal a savage blow to us all. But we must be prepared to look dangers and death in the face. We are supposed to be heroes, and heroes we shall try to be. This is our last evening here on these shores which we shall not see again for many moons. We have here a fine feast prepared, so let's get on and enjoy it like proper heroes."

Again there was a resounding cheer and the Argonauts set about the feast with great relish. The shadows of evening were lengthening along the shore as we gathered foliage from nearby and spread it along the beach, well away from the lapping of the waves. The palace servants had arrived with oil-lamps, platters of appetizing food and pitchers of the best wines from the palace cellars. There were some expert butchers among our company, and my two oxen provided excellent cuts of meat. As the wine loosened their tongues, the revellers recounted to each other many tales of gods and heroes from times gone by. And there was much singing and jollity.

As for me, I felt tired and a little depressed. I wandered away and sat down beneath *Argo*'s Dodonian-oak prow. What had I let myself in for? Here was a boat, untried yet on the seas, and a band of well meaning but (for the most part) inexperienced sailors, setting out on a journey to far-off mysterious lands to retrieve a Golden Fleece guarded most probably by savages and a fearsome monster, and...

"Hello, there," interrupted a drunken voice. "Having a fit of the glooms, are we, old boy? Tummy turning over, is it, and playing cowardy-cowardy custard? But fear not, little Jason, for you see here this spear, held by Idas himself, which will protect you more surely than could even Zeus himself. Yes, I am Idas, the invincible, and with me at your side, have no fears that we may not succeed, however many gods might threaten us on our way."

I was amazed at his impudence, but particularly at his complete lack of reverence for the gods. I was not the only one. I became aware that all the Argonauts had heard his speech, and the silence which followed it was broken by the voice of Idmon:

"You are drunk, Idas, and obviously cannot hold your drink. No proper hero would let wine cause him to blaspheme against the gods. Let me remind you of what happened to the sons of Aloeus, Otus and Ephialtes. In fact, they were really the sons of Poseidon, and they were bigger than you, little Idas. In fact by the time they were only nine years old, they were each over fifty feet high. They boasted that they intended to pile Mount Ossa on top of Mount Olympus and Mount Pelion over there on top of Ossa, until they reached heaven itself. But my father, Apollo, killed them first before they could even reach manhood. So just you watch your step, my lad."

Idas scowled at Idmon, and continued with his insolence:

"Oh, you think you're a clever prophet, do you? Well then, prophesy me this: will I suffer the same fate as did Photis and Eliphates? Get it wrong and then prophesy me how you'll escape this spear here for getting it wrong, eh? Prophesy me that, you silly old prophet!"

"Enough!" I cried. "Someone throw a bucket of water over Idas here, and Orpheus, dear Orpheus, please lift your lyre and sing us one of your ballads."

No sooner had Orpheus started than all was cool and calm. Even Idas began to smile as Idmon dried his hair for him. Orpheus was obviously going to be a great asset on our journey.

He sang of how heaven and sea, once joined together, separated after deadly strife; how the stars and moon and sun found their places in the sky; how the mountains grew and how rivers ran; the coming of nymphs and of all creeping things; how Ophion and Eurynome first ruled snowy Olympus; then how they fell into the waters of Ocean, supplanted by Cronos and Rhea, who then ruled over the happy Titans; the childhood of Zeus in the Dictaean cave, before the earthborn Cyclopes had armed him with his bolts, the thunder and lightning which founded his majestic power.

The song came to an end, but there was not a sound from the revellers. Such was the enchantment of Orpheus's music that it lingered on as they sat there under his spell, and soon all began to nod off. I had watched Idas carefully during Orpheus's song, and noticed that he paled visibly when the tale of strife ended with mention of Zeus's bolts. I went over to him and said:

"I hope you feel better now. Have a good night's sleep, because we shall need your great strength at your oar tomorrow."

A few of us mixed libations to Zeus, according to the usual rite, and poured them over the tongues of flame on the altar.

I curled up under some foliage and fell into deep slumber.

24

We're off!

Once again, rosy-fingered dawn crept stealthily over Pelion's ridge and streaked the bay of Pagasae with gold. Apollo was doing us proud as far as the weather was concerned.

Tiphys was the first to wake, and he wasted no time is rousing the crew. He climbed on to the quarterdeck and shouted:

"On board, everyone! Find your allotted bench, stow your gear and prepare your oars for rowing!"

Heracles and Ancaeus were first on board, and *Argo* groaned under their weight. I saw Argus wince but he said nothing. When, after much cursing and complaining, all the others were in place, Argus asked me to climb down into the water again and look at some marks on the side of the galley where the water-level lapped against them.

"Which mark is showing above the water?" he asked.

"I can see three marks," I replied, "one above the other."

"That's fine," said Argus as I clambered back up the steps above the cutwater and joined him on the foredeck.

"Please explain," I said, somewhat irritably.

"I thought you'd never ask," continued Argus with an apology for a grin on his face. "There are five marks altogether, each one six vertical inches apart. If I have calculated correctly, the water level should be at the bottom mark when the vessel is unloaded, at the centre mark when loaded normally, with oarsmen and all gear and provisions. If ever the top mark is exceeded, then *Argo* will be overloaded and in danger of shipping excess water in the event of rough seas. In that case we would have to reduce the weight on board."

"Very ingenious, sir, if I may say so," I replied. "You seem to have thought of everything."

"That would be impossible," said Argus. "My design calculations have been meticulous, but only time will tell whether they are adequate. We have many days ahead, and the seas will test both *Argo* and her crew to the limit."

Then, to my surprise, Acastus suddenly got up from his bench, climbed onto the central gangway and invited Argus and me to join him on the quarterdeck. We walked down the gangway and joined him there where Tiphys, Orpheus,

Zetes and Calais were already standing. Acastus drew a golden chalice from beneath his marvellous double-folded cloak.

"I hope you don't mind, but I brought this with me from my father's palace. I thought you might use it to pour suitable libations of wine over the sea."

My heart warmed to him from that moment. I thanked him for his thoughtfulness, and did as he suggested. Then, as I had planned, I prayed aloud to Zeus, and called upon the winds and the swift-running currents of the seas, and upon all our nights and days to be kind to us and bring us safely back home again.

Suddenly, from the direction of Pelion, we heard an auspicious clap of thunder, and—even more amazing—*Argo* herself shouted: "Here we go!" You may remember that the oak beam at the front of the prow was provided by the goddess Athena from the sacred oak which grows in the sanctuary of Zeus at Dodona in Epirus, and was endowed with the gift of speech.

Argus actually smiled, or I think he did. He was proud of his ship, and particularly of the help which Athena had given him when building it.

Mopsus, who had taken up position on his bench, stood up and declared that all the omens were good. He came from Thessaly and had fought in the battle between the Lapiths and the centaurs. He could understand the language of birds, having been taught their language by Apollo himself. He was one of our two soothsayers on the expedition, the other being Idmon who also confirmed the declaration of Mopsus.

Then, without waiting to be asked, Argus and Acastus left us on the quarterdeck and took up their proper places at their oars. Zetes and Calais, on my instructions, went forward to the foredeck as lookouts; my idea was that they could, from there, more easily fly ahead to look for submerged rocks and other such obstructions and dangers. Orpheus perched himself on a little seat which Argus had provided for him at the port side of the quarterdeck, just behind the crossbar which held the belaying pins. Tiphys took up his position towards the front of the quarterdeck where he could control one or both steering oars.

I gave the order to cast off, and Zetes and Calais drew in the hawsers.

"Are your oars at the ready, men?" I cried.

"Get on with it!" said some unidentified wag.

"Right then," I responded. "Ready?...Steady!...Row!"

Chaos!

Some dug their oars in so deep that they couldn't easily get them out again. Others missed the sea altogether and ended up in the lap of the rower behind them and with their legs waving in the air. Heracles did well—so well in fact that his oar finished almost level with the side of the *Argo*, and he had to lift it off its thole-pin before he could recover it.

Tiphys cursed them all and told them to get back to the ready position as soon as possible.

"Heroes and demi-gods you may be," he shouted, "but rowers most of you ain't!"

"Now listen carefully," he continued. "Fortunately you have an experienced oarsman among your number, Asterion, and by good luck he has been allotted the port-side bench immediately in front of me here. So you can all see him, can't you? Right then, he will show you the technique of rowing, but in very slow motion to start with. Follow him exactly, particularly how he twists his blade at each stage of the stroke.

"When I say ROW ONE, you will all perform one stroke only and then rest your oars.

"Wait for it...ROW ONE!"

Believe it or not, all went surprisingly well. Even Heracles restrained himself from excessive exertion.

"Well done!" cried Tiphys.

And a tremendous cheer arose from the large crowd on the sea-front, because, at last, *Argo* was actually on the move.

Tiphys continued his lessons, and *Argo* slowly but surely gathered speed. Once the crew got the hang of it, and a good rowing rhythm had been established, Tiphys handed over the timing of the strokes to Orpheus who gave the beat as an integral part of his music. Accompanied by his lyre, he sang of Artemis, guardian of ships and of Pelion's peaks which looked down on us as we made our way southward down the gulf of Pagasae. I had never been on a ship before, and I found the experience quite idyllic. I was looking back wistfully at the retreating shore, when my gaze was drawn to the long and glistening white wake of *Argo*, which resembled a gleaming path stretching over an azure plain. And then there were shoals of fish, both large and small, which leaped in and out of the foaming wake, obviously enchanted by the strains of Orpheus's lyre; they reminded me of the sheep I had left behind on Pelion's slopes, following their shepherd as he played his reedy pipe.

Tiphys steered a course close to the Magnesian coastline and it was not long before we reached a point where the path from Cheiron's School for Heroes came down to meet the shore. And sure enough, who should there be standing on the beach with the waves lapping round his fetlocks but Cheiron himself, waving at us like mad and shouting his good wishes for our adventure.

Behind him at the water's edge was his wife, Chariclo, holding the baby Achilles high above her head so that his father could see him.

Peleus was at his oar on the port side, five benches forward from the quarterdeck. I told him to raise and ship his oar so that he could stand up and wave back. He did more than that. He came up onto the quarterdeck and waved and waved until Achilles and his minders were mere specks on the seashore. He had tears in his eyes as he returned to his bench and resumed his rowing. All right—I must confess that I too had tears in my eyes; I was saying farewell, probably for ever, to my first twenty years on that wonderful Magnesian peninsula and the many friends I had made there.

"Are we going to row all the way to the land of the Golden Fleece, Captain, or do you think we could take advantage of what may be a rare breeze to fill our sail?"

Tiphys was staring closely at me, and I blushed, knowing that my tears betrayed my feelings.

"Only asking, Captain," he continued. "Would you like me to get the sail hoisted now?"

I suddenly realised how inexperienced I was in nautical matters, and how dependent I was on the skills of my crew.

"Of course, Tiphys," I replied. "You will have to excuse my incompetence for a while, I'm afraid, until I get the hang of things. Please carry on."

With admirable authority Tiphys organised the shipping of the oars, and then the stepping of the mast and the hoisting of our square sail. Each member of the crew was allotted his appropriate task so that he would know exactly what to do on this and any future occasion.

We all had to learn the names of the various items of gear—the **step** (the block into which the mast fitted and held it secure), the **backstay** (the rope from the top of the mast back to the quarterdeck), the **yard** (the wooden pole from which the sail was suspended), the **halyard** (the rope used for hoisting the yard up to the top of the mast), the **port** (left-hand side looking forward) and **starboard** (right-hand side), **braces** (ropes from the ends of the yard back to the belaying (holding) pins at the front of the quarterdeck), the **buntlines** (ropes which were used for furling and unfurling the sail)—and quite a few more!

The crew were quick to learn and (such was Tiphys's air of authority) obedient, and in about twenty-four minutes the sail had been raised, the sail unfurled and billowing magnificently in the firm north-westerly breeze.

The crew were now able to relax. Many of them preferred to stay at their allotted positions, but some of them wandered to the foredeck or quarterdeck, which initially became somewhat crowded. But I decided to let the crew sort themselves out, and that indeed is what they did.

We were on our way, and sailing!

25

The Aegean Sea!

"When we leave the gulf of Pagasae," said Tiphys, "we shall have to turn almost due east for some way before we turn northwards up the east coast of Magnesia."

"So?" I replied.

"So," continued Tiphys, "unless the wind veers from the west and then from the south, we shall have to furl the sail and resume rowing."

"I see," I replied, not knowing what else to say.

"May I make a suggestion concerning the rowing?" said Tiphys.

"Please do," I replied.

Actually, I was finding it difficult to give him my full attention, because I was busy at the time in trying to remove a wood-splinter from Peleus. He seemed to have picked one up accidentally from his rowing bench.

"Impossible," interrupted Argus.

"Excuse me a moment, Tiphys," I said, turning to Argus. "What is impossible?"

"Peleus getting a splinter from one of my benches." replied Argus. "They were all planed and polished smooth by me personally."

He wandered away, and I saw him inspecting Peleus's bench.

"What I suggest," continued Tiphys, somewhat irritably, "is that you divide the crew of fifty rowers into five teams of ten rowers each. Then, when we resume rowing, one team can be relaxing off-duty while the other four row. Each team can take it in turns to relax for say fifteen minutes at a time. This means that no team would row continuously for more than an hour, thereby conserving their strength. However, when needs demand, for example when we meet savage currents such as those we shall meet in the narrows at each end of the sea of Marmora, we can revert to full power with all five teams rowing at the same time."

"Anyone can make a mistake," said Argus, and he walked off, adze in hand, down the central gangway back to Peleus's bench.

"Thank you," said Peleus. "I must say that ointment you used is pleasant, though not of course strictly necessary." He walked away smiling.

"Well?" asked Tiphys.

"An excellent suggestion, Tiphys," I replied. "I'll organise it as you say immediately."

It was a sheer delight to have a helmsman with such a high degree of numeracy and organisational skills. However, I thought it politic to acquaint Argus of the plan before I started on its implementation.

"You will make sure," he said, "that each team of ten consists of five rowers on the port and five rowers on the starboard sides, and that they are preferably opposite each other on the same bench, won't you?"

I was about to walk off in a huff when I detected the glimmer of a smile. He was pulling my leg.

"Good heavens," I said. "I would never have thought of that. Thanks for the advice."

I think I was beginning to get the hang of Argus.

And so things were organised shortly before we left the gulf and, as we did so, Tiphys steered the *Argo* eastwards along the south coast of the Magnesian peninsula. The northerly breeze was useless, so we furled the sail with the buntlines and resumed rowing with forty oars with Peleus's team taking their turn for the first quarter-hour of off-duty.

After an hour and a half I suggested to Tiphys that the crew had had enough for the first day and he agreed. When we spotted a beach suitable for landing, with what looked like a spring coming down from the high ground behind it, we rowed for the shore, beached *Argo* and prepared for an evening meal. Some of the crew replenished our water supply while others foraged for food and still others gathered foliage to keep us warm as we slept under the shelter of trees above the beach.

Next morning we had hoped for a westerly breeze, but we were unlucky. Immediately after breakfast Tiphys said, "Let's be shooting off then!" And so we named the beach *Aphetai Argous* or *Argo's Offshoot*.

We resumed rowing and after a few hours we had passed the channel between the mainland and the island of Skiathos. Cape Sepias came into view and Peleus (who was off-duty at the time) pointed out the cave where he had been dyed with sepia ink by Thetis and later lived with her as his wife. The crew all cheered and Peleus laughed. But I could see that his laughter was forced and I tried to divert his thoughts by asking:

"Hey, do I feel a southerly breeze developing?"

Tiphys commented that the prospect of a southerly had been obvious for the last half hour.

Sure enough, the breeze was gathering strength. We shipped oars and unfurled the sail again. It was thrilling to see it fill and to feel the thrust of the wind as we sped northwards along the Magnesian coast.

By nightfall we had reached the coast to the east of mount Ossa, and we beached near the tomb of Dolops who was a son of Hermes. We offered a burnt sacrifice of sheep in his honour (and enjoyed the meal naturally) but it did us no good; the wind veered against us and we were stuck there for three nights. We could have rowed of course, but we had reached the part of our journey where we had to cross some sea, rather than hugging the coast which was to be our strategy for as much of the voyage as possible. We decided to wait for a fair wind, and a south-westerly developed during the third night.

At crack of dawn Tiphys again said, "Let's be shooting off then!" and another beach was bequeathed with name of *Aphetai*!

We followed the coast as far as we could but we veered off north-eastward when we saw Mount Olympus in the distance to our left. Then, as luck or the gods would have it, the wind veered and changed to a strong westerly, and then we were flying.

We reached Cape Poseidon (the tip of the western prong of the Khalkhidiki peninsula trident) by nightfall and we could have anchored for the night, but Tiphys was for carrying on while the westerly wind was with us. On through the night we sped along, with *Argo*'s structure being tested to its limits. By dawn we were south of Mount Athos (on the tip of the eastern prong of the peninsula's trident), and still Tiphys was for carrying on. The crew did not complain; they knew there would be more than enough opportunity for them to row in the days to come!

All through that day and night we flew, but, as the next dawn crept over the eastern horizon, the wind dropped and we were becalmed. However, straight ahead, as we shielded our eyes against the sun, we could see an island.

"That," announced Tiphys, "is Lemnos. I suggest that we row there, replenish our stores and stay overnight. We need a good night's rest after all that sailing. We shall make for the harbour of a city called Myrine on its west coast. I believe the king there is called Thoas and he is reputed to be friendly. Perhaps we can sleep indoors for a change."

I agreed. Trying to sleep on board at night was difficult in *Argo*'s rather cramped accommodation.

So we furled the sail and rowed. As we approached the harbour, we could see scores of warriors in full armour streaming out of the city gates, and spreading out along the beach of the harbour, waving their spears and shrieking like we had never heard warriors shriek before. There were one hundred and forty-nine of them.

We were not expecting that.

26

The Isle of Lemnos

"What the heck do we do now?" I asked Tiphys.

"You're the skipper," he replied. "I'm only the helmsman. You decide!"

"Thank you very much," I said. "I shall send Zetes and

Calais to fly over them and frighten them a bit. And then we can use Aethalides, our herald. He can go and find out if the Lemnians have a problem."

Aethalides, I should mention, was the son of Hermes and Eupolemeia, and half-brother of Echion and Eurytus who were also among the crew. His father had given him the gift of perfect memory, and he also was endowed with the ability to fabricate truths at will without actually telling lies, a gift much admired and cultivated by politicians. He was also an outstanding archer, well able to look after himself. Just the man to send forward to see what the Lemnians wanted.

I asked Lynceus to report on things because he had the sharpest eyesight I have ever known. I told him to watch the expressions on the faces of the Lemnian warriors as Zetes and Calais flew over them and as Aethalides talked with their leader.

We beached in the shallows of the harbour and Aethalides climbed down the steps at the prow into the water, waded ashore and started talking to the warrior wearing the most impressive armour, presumably the leader.

"They all look frightened and relieved," reported Lynceus. "In fact they are turning round now and going back towards the town. Aethalides is coming back now."

"Yes, Lynceus," I said. "I can see that. It was just the expressions on their faces that I wanted to know about. Anyway, thank you for your help."

"Don't mention it," said Lynceus.

Aethalides climbed back on board.

"It's all right," he reported. "We can stay the night. They thought we were a band of enemy Thracians come to attack them, but I explained who we were and all about our expedition. And guess what?"

"I give in," I said. "Get on with it."

"They are all of them women—not a man anywhere!"

I turned to Lyncaeus and asked him why he had not noticed that the warriors had no beards.

"Of course I noticed that," he said. "I'm not blind, you know. You asked me to report on their expressions, not their shaving habits."

"Why have they gone back to the city?" I asked Aethalides.

"They didn't say," he replied, "but their leader said she would contact us again once we were all ashore."

By the time we had disembarked and I was wondering whether to tell the crew to prepare to settle down on the beach, I saw a girl returning from the city, obviously with a message for me.

"My name is Iphinoe," she said to me when she arrived on the beach. "Queen Hypsipyle has had a meeting with the assembly of citizens and they have asked me to report to you what they have decided. She requests your presence in her palace where she has an important proposal to put to you. If your crew can be patient, the citizens will shortly be driving down to this beach in their pony-carts to transport them back to the town where they will be fed and entertained and accommodated overnight."

"This is a real royal welcome," said Argus to me. "But before you go with Iphinoe to talk with Queen Hypsipyle, I have something for you."

He climbed back on board the *Argo*, and came back carrying the most magnificent cloak you could possibly imagine. It was made of crimson cloth, of double width, with a brilliant purple border. But the edges all round were embroidered with a panoply of scenes from mythology.

"Athena gave me this for our captain to wear on prestigious occasions. This is certainly one of them, and I suggest you wear it for your reception by the queen."

"I am flattered and grateful to Athena for this wonderful cloak," I replied. "It will give me confidence."

"And for heaven's sake," said Argus, "leave behind that crude spear you insist on carrying, and change it for that magnificent slender spear which Atalanta presented to you to show she had no hard feelings when you said she couldn't come on this expedition because she would upset the concentration of our all-male crew."

"Thanks for reminding me, old pal," I responded. "All right, I'll take it. I must confess it will create a better impression than my usual spear."

And so equipped with cloak and spear, I set off with Iphinoe, feeling rather magnificent, and with justification, to judge from the expressions on the faces of the Lemnian girls as I entered the city gates.

As I approached the palace, its double doors were thrown open by the palace maids. Iphinoe escorted me through the entrance hall and invited me to sit on a gleaming couch. I did so and when I looked up I found that I was facing her mistress, Queen Hypsipyle.

27

Queen Hypsipyle

I watched Hypsipyle closely, since even then I could not rule out that we might have been led into a trap. But I saw that she was, in fact, blushing—not a sign to indicate that we were in any kind of danger.

"Welcome, stranger," she said, eyeing me all over. "That's a handsome spear you have there, if I may be so bold. Where did you get that from?"

I told her about Atalanta and she laughed: "I bet you wish you had brought her with you now. It must get very lonely on board a ship with only fifty men for company."

"Fifty-four actually," I replied, "but it did not seem sensible to have a crew of fifty-five men and a girl, especially one like Atalanta who would probably kill any one of us who tried any nonsense."

"Like that, was she?" replied. "Oh dear. Well, never mind. You have come to the right place now."

"You appear to like my spear," I said, "but what about this cloak?"

"Very nice, I'm sure," she replied somewhat distantly.

"Perhaps I should mention that this cloak was a gift from the goddess Athena herself," I said.

Hypsipyle turned pale. "It's absolutely magnificent," she responded. "It really is the most magnificent cloak I have ever seen."

"It really is," she went on, pretending to inspect it closely, and walking round me to make sure that she was seen to be interested, just in case Athena was somewhere around (you can never tell with goddesses—or gods for that matter).

"Anyway," she continued when she had resumed her place on her throne, "I believe from your herald Aethalides that you are Jason and your companions are a noble band of adventurers called Argonauts who are starting on a quest to recover a Golden Fleece from far distant lands. But let me explain who we are, and why we are all women here in this city, and why we greeted you in full warrior armour. I'll keep it brief so that we don't keep you and your comrades waiting to receive our hospitality.

"A few years ago, when Thoas my father was king of this city, Myrine, and the whole of the isle of Lemnos, our men used to amuse themselves by raiding the coastal regions of the mainland of Thrace to the north of here. They brought back bags of booty and young girls as slaves. And then the goddess Aphrodite intervened. As you no doubt know from your study of mythology, Aphrodite is married to the god Hephaestus who has one of his forges here on the north coast of this island and who was annoyed with our men for not concentrating on our traditional skill of metalworking; I expect you noticed the superb armour we were wearing when we came to greet you! Anyway, Aphrodite also was annoyed with our men for robbing the Thracians of their young girls, so she afflicted them with a loathing of us, their legitimate wives, and an all-embracing passion for their girl captives. They turned us out of our homes. Our own children were either turned out with us or kept at home with their newly-acquired stepmothers who practised all kinds of cruelty on them and neglected them terribly, preferring the children they had borne to our ex-husbands."

"How dreadful!" I commented.

"Indeed it was," Hypsipyle continued. "It got so bad that we wives got together and conceived a cunning plan. One day, while the men were engaged on yet another expedition to Thrace, we turned all their Thracian trollops out of the city and locked all the city gates. When they returned, they begged us to forgive them and let them in. But we could see that they were still infatuated by their girls. So we struck a deal with them. They agreed to leave Lemnos to us women, and we would let them take back with them all the male children from our city."

"What happened to your father, Thoas?" I asked her.

She looked puzzled for a moment and then replied, "Oh, he died soon afterwards. Yes, and so you see we were a city of women only, but we soon learnt how to farm and carry on the metal-working skills which we needed to maintain our trade in armaments throughout the northern Aegean.

"But to be quite honest, we do need men again. The arrival of your party of over fifty of the most noble men in the world is most timely. Why don't you all settle down here with us and make this your home? And, to be quite honest with you, I've taken a great fancy to you, really. You could be king here and I could be queen, and you could forget all about this stupid quest of yours for some Golden Fleece. What good will that do you, even if you survive the perils of the quest and actually return to Iolcos with it?"

All this rather stunned me. My mind turned over what

I had learnt from Cheiron and all my promises to my parents and the heroes for whom I was responsible.

"Queen Hypsipyle," I eventually replied, "I am greatly flattered and attracted by your proposal, but I'm afraid I cannot accept. I have made promises and sworn oaths, and I must keep them. However, we do need your help and we accept your generous offer of hospitality before we resume our journey."

"I quite understand," she replied. "We look forward to your stay with us."

Hypsipyle told Iphinoe to tell the citizens to escort all the Argonauts from the harbour into the city. I went down with her and told my crew what had been agreed. They jumped at the invitation, especially when they saw the women of Myrine coming to fetch them in their smooth-running horse-drawn buggies which were overflowing with all kinds of goodies—fruits and other delicacies, wine-skins and embroidered cloaks for them to wear.

But not Heracles. "There's something not quite right here," he said. "You lot go off and enjoy yourselves, but be careful. Women can be tricky."

"I know that," I responded. "We can look after ourselves, you know."

"No I don't," he said. "However, I'll stay here and look after our good ship *Argo*, if you don't mind."

"Thanks," I said, as Peleus sauntered up to me.

"You look ridiculous in that cloak," he said.

"Maybe," I replied, "but it worked on Hypsipyle. She wants to marry me, and what do you think of that?"

"Not a lot," he said. "But I rather fancy my chances here, you know."

"No I don't," I replied, remembering Heracles's wit. "Anyway, you watch your step, old pal. I refused her offer, of course, but a day or two's rest here will be most welcome to the crew, I'm sure."

Little did I realise what was in store for us.

28

Languishing on Lemnos

And so we were all transported to the city in great style. Heracles, joined by Zetes and Calais, the twin sons of the North Wind, stayed with the *Argo*. The rest of the crew dispersed to the homes of their hosts to be entertained by them and I returned to the palace where Hypsipyle was waiting for me.

"I have organised," she announced, "a grand dance and banquet. The songs and sacrifices will be in honour of Hephaestus and Aphrodite. You and your crew are invited to attend."

The day was far spent, and as we walked out into main square of the city, I could see that the tables were already prepared for a feast, torches were blazing and fires had been lit ready for the burnt offerings.

My crew and their newly-acquired girl-friends were already arriving and before long the celebrations were in full swing.

This was certainly the most exciting occasion I had experienced since the wedding of Peleus and Thetis many years before. What I did not realise at the time (but realised later) was that we had all (with the exception of Heracles and his two companions) been almost completely enchanted by Aphrodite. It is difficult to describe how I (and presumably the others) felt (drunk with desire, frantic with fervour, unhinged with hysteria?). Somehow we all knew we were not ourselves but were too weak-willed to snap out of it.

Day followed day and week followed week (I actually lost count) until one day Heracles arrived in the square, brandishing his great club, with Zetes and Calais buzzing round threateningly in the sky above us.

"You will all," he shouted, and, I mean, **shouted**, "attend a meeting outside the city walls with me, and you will not bring any of these ladies with you. Now!"

In spite of our headaches, we obeyed. If you had ever seen Heracles and his club, you would have done the same. We staggered our way out of the square, down the main street and through the city gates.

Heracles climbed on to a large mound by the side of the road (he need not have bothered) and addressed us:

"Call yourselves heroes, you lily-livered load of layabouts! Have you forgotten what we are supposed to be doing? Do you expect to find the Golden Fleece here under one of your trollops' beds? We may as well all go home now, and leave Jason here to repopulate the whole of Lemnos."

"However," he continued, when he had cooled down a little, "I suppose we must suspect Aphrodite had something to do with it. I suspect that both she and Hephaestus, together with all the Lemnian ladies, wanted to ensure the return of male offspring to Lemnos. No doubt your stay here will have achieved that objective. So now let us now return to our good ship *Argo*, and get on with our expedition."

You could have heard a pin drop. The colour of my face was best described as beetroot. Looking round my band of heroes, I had never seen so many mouths O-shaped.

Without another word spoken, we stumbled our way down to the harbour.

And then, as we were preparing to get on board the *Argo*, the women of Lemnos sensed our intentions. They came flying down from the city gates and swarmed round us like bees from a hive.

The scene now contrasted sharply with the scene which greeted us on our arrival. The shining armour and flashing swords were now replaced by women in gorgeous garments embracing our heroes with tears flowing freely. But they were not imploring us to stay; rather they were saying fond farewells and praying for our safe return.

Hypsipyle rushed up to me and flung herself into my arms.

"You win, my darling," she cried. "We cannot expect you and your heroes to betray your calling to recover the Golden Fleece and to bring back the ghost of Phrixus. How else can your homeland hope to prosper? We understand that now. But when you have achieved all your objectives, please remember us. There will always be a welcome for you here, and my father's throne is yours for the asking.

"But on a personal note: if the gods bless me with a child of yours while you are away, please tell me now what you would like me to do with him!"

I was unable to reply for some while. When I had recovered my composure, I said:

"Thank you, Hypsipyle, for your kindness and understanding. May all your prayers be answered, and may you and your country prosper. Our journey will be a perilous one. I hope we shall all return to our homeland, but if not, if I am not destined to return home, please, if you bear me a son, could you send him to my father's palace at Aesonis, so that he can be a comfort and protection for my dear parents?"

"Certainly," she replied, "but I pray that will not be necessary. I shall need him to succeed me as King of Lemnos! But in any case, do look in on us on your journey home with the Golden Fleece. You can be sure of a royal welcome, and you have already tasted our hospitality."

"I look forward to that," I said.

I embraced her and we said our farewells.

And so the Argonauts once again climbed on board the *Argo* and the forty whose turn it was to row manned their oars. I loosed the stern-cable from the anchor-rock, Tiphys gave the order to row and Orpheus set the rhythm.

"Where now?" I asked Tiphys.

"Orpheus suggests we call in at the isle of Samothrace on our way to the Hellespont," he replied. "It's a little out of our way, and we shall steer east-north-east rather than due east, but he says that Samothrace is the isle of Electra, daughter of Atlas and one of the Pleiades. There are secret rites there which celebrate the mysteries of the Cabiri. He says that we shall all sail in greater safety and with greater confidence if we are initiated."

And that is what we did. I would like to have given you details, but the rites were secret, so you will have to remain in ignorance. Sorry!

On leaving Samothrace, we steered south-east towards the mouth of the Hellespont.

Peleus was off-duty for a while on this leg of the journey, and said he would like a chat.

"What about?" I asked him.

"About Hypsipyle," he replied, "and all those women. You realise now, of course, that their account of why there were no men on the island was a load of lies."

"How do you mean?" I asked.

"Well," he replied, "they didn't banish their husbands and their girlfriends to Thrace."

"What did they do, then?" I asked.

"They murdered the whole lot of them," said Peleus.

29

Through the Hellespont

"M-m-m-urdered them?" I stammered.

"Yes," replied Peleus. "Murdered all of them, including all male children, so that they could not grow up and avenge the deaths of their fathers. Oh, there was one exception. Hypsipyle saved her father, King Thoas, because she put him in a chest and put him out to sea. He survived apparently; some fishermen dragged him ashore on the island of Oenoe."

"How come you know all this?" I asked.

"Well, some women talk in their sleep," he said, "especially when they have had too much wine."

"And why didn't you tell me as soon as you found out the truth?" I asked him.

"There was no point," he replied. "In any case you would probably have thrown a wobbly and upset the apple cart."

"Thank you very much," I responded, "for your confidence in my leadership abilities."

"All right, he said, "I'm sorry. But things turned out for the best as it happened. We had a relaxing holiday and the Lemnian ladies achieved their objective of ensuring the next generation of men to safeguard the future of Lemnos."

I thought a while. Then I asked, "What did they do with all the bodies?"

"You remember," Peleus replied, "when Heracles harangued us outside the city?"

"I shall find it difficult to forget it," I replied.

"Well," said Peleus, "you remember that he climbed on a mound so we could see him even better? Well, that was their funeral mound."

"It's your shift to row, by the look of it," I said.

I walked to the rail at the rear of the quarterdeck, leant over and wept. So much for the confidence instilled by the Cabirian mysteries, though I must confess that they worked in the longer term. After a while I felt a hand on my shoulder but I did not dare look round immediately for fear of embarrassment. When I did, I saw it was Argus.

"Carry on, Captain," he said with the hint of a smile.

And I had to do just that. A decision had soon to be made. We had just passed by the isle of Imbros (modern Gökçeada) on our starboard side and were rapidly approaching the neck of the Hellespont where the strong currents of the waters originating from the Black Sea, after flowing through the Sea of Marmara (the Propontis), rush through the long and narrow strait of the Hellespont and out into the great Aegean Sea.

As we approached the foreland of the Chersonese (the long spit of land jutting out from Thrace and now, I believe, known as the Dardanelles), the sun was setting and Tiphys asked for a decision. "There is a strong south-westerly blowing up and, since the moon is rising and will help my navigation, perhaps we should take advantage of both wind and moon and tackle the Hellespont now under full sail and all fifty oars. However, I know we planned to spend the night ashore and the men have been rowing on and off all day. But we may not get another chance for a long time to defeat these fiendish currents. What do you think?"

Argus (who had been listening) agreed: "Well, that's what I designed the *Argo* for—to defeat currents like these under full power. I think we may need all the sail power we can get to supplement *Argo*'s fifty oars."

I put the matter to the crew, saying that my preference was for carrying on under full power, taking advantage of the wind and moonlight. Some of the crew were a little grumpy (they were looking forward to a good night's sleep) but the majority were for it, no doubt inspired by the mysteries in which they had recently participated.

And so, under full power, we tackled the Hellespont throughout the night and succeeded. By dawn we had left behind the worst of the currents and the Sea of Marmara broadened out in front on us. The crew rested their oars and we carried on under the billowing sail. After one night's rest ashore we resumed sailing on the following day and the wind which had veered to a westerly did us proud.

Keeping the southern (Asian) shore on our starboard side, we eventually reached a harbour called Fairhaven, where Tiphys had heard rumour that the natives were friendly.

We were not disappointed.

30

Cyzicus and the Doliones

The sea of Marmara, if you were an eagle soaring really high and peering down, would seem to you to be shaped like a large and rather knobbly lemon, with the Hellespont like a stalk at its western end, and the Bosporus and the Clashing Rocks (as we were to discover later) blocking the way into the Black Sea, at its eastern end.

Halfway along the southern coast of this lemon there is a large island, shaped like a squat inverted pyramid, which juts northwards into the sea of Marmara, and is noted for a large mountain with several peaks covering most of the island, called Mount Dindymon, known locally as Bear Mountain. Strictly speaking it is not actually an island because it is joined to the mainland plain to the south by a shallow isthmus.

The south of the island, the isthmus and the plain were inhabited by a people called the Doliones and their king was called Cyzicus and their city, situated on the south of the island at the northern end on the isthmus, was also called Cyzicus after their king.

About four miles to the west of the city is a small port called Artaki (modern Erdek), whose harbour was known as Fairhaven, and it was into this harbour that we sailed late that afternoon.

We were uncertain whether to drop anchor here or to sail further towards better shelter nearer the isthmus, so we waited in the hope that the local people might turn up to advise us and (hopefully) offer us food and shelter.

In less than an hour a reception committee appeared on horseback from the direction of Cyzicus city, and hailed us from the harbour wall.

"Ahoy there!" said their leader. "My name is Cyzicus, king of the Doliones. You are welcome here and we offer you our hospitality. We have been advised by an oracle to expect the arrival of a godlike band of heroes, and here you are."

Tiphys was on the point of dropping our anchor-stone when Cyzicus shouted, "Stop! Do not drop anchor here. It will be much safer if you sail a few miles along the coast and drop anchor in the city harbour near the isthmus. In any case, your anchor-stone is much too small for safety. We have a much larger and better stone here."

"What a load of rubbish," muttered Argus so that only I could hear. "Our stone is quite adequate. However, I suppose we had better humour him."

We pulled close to the harbour wall and swapped stones. Cyzicus said he would like to keep our old smaller stone as a memento of our visit. (Strangely enough, very many years later the island was inhabited by settlers from Pylos in the Peloponnese and they installed this stone as a sacred relic in a temple to Jasonian Athena!)

And so we sailed to the city harbour and built an altar on the beach for Apollo, the god of 'Happy Landings' and prepared a suitable sacrifice.

That evening we spent very pleasantly in King Cyzicus's palace. It was a 'men only' affair. Cyzicus was, in fact, on his honeymoon, having recently married Cleite, a noble lady and the daughter of Merops of Percote. So we felt very honoured by his time spent with us. He wined and dined us and wanted to know everything about us and our expedition. We in turn asked him about the geography of our eastward journey. He told us a lot about the towns and peoples of the southern coast of the Propontis, but concerning the Bosporus and our chances of getting into the Black Sea he could tell us next to nothing.

We asked him about the coast-line to the east, and he advised us to climb Mount Dindymon next morning, from the peak of which, he said, we could get a superb view of most of the Sea of Marmara.

"But beware," he continued. "Mount Dindymon is also called Bear Mountain, because it is inhabited by a tribe of savage creatures. I doubt if you would ever see anything like them again. They have six great arms, two springing from their shoulders and the other four from their thick thighs. They never bother us. Poseidon, our ancestor, protects us from them. But with strangers like yourselves they may prove unpredictable."

We assured him that we could look after ourselves.

So, next morning, a large band of us, twenty-one in number, set out to climb the west side of the mountain. Cyzicus's warning was not an empty one. The monsters swarmed down from the eastern flank and began hurling rocks into the sea to the west of the *Argo*, trying to block it in the harbour. The thirty-four Argonauts we had left behind at the harbour, including the mighty Heracles, were hard pressed to contain the onslaught of these savages. Meanwhile my party of twenty-one, before we had reached the summit, heard the shouting; Lyncaeus, who had the sharpest eyesight I have ever experienced, saw quite clearly what was happening. We raced back to the harbour. Iphiclus, my maternal uncle, who could race against the winds and run over a field of corn and not crush it, got there first of course. As soon as we arrived we joined in the battle.

We won. We killed all the monsters, and laid their corpses in a long line along the beach at the water's edge. Peleus wandered up to me.

"How many do you think there are there?" he asked.

"Ninety-nine exactly," I replied.

"Strange," he responded. "I reckon there are six hundred arms there."

"You are not going to tell me you counted all their arms," I said sarcastically, believing that his method of counting was limited to 'one, two, three, lots'.

"I never said I did," he replied, "but that's what I reckon. Not that it matters." And off he sauntered. I double-checked, and, yes, there were one hundred.

Argus had been listening to our conversation. "Don't worry," he said. "While you were counting the bodies the first time, I saw somebody, who shall remain nameless, retrieving a dead monster which had been hidden by the bushes and adding it to the beginning of the line."

I thanked Argus. My confidence in myself was restored,

and counted myself fortunate in my friends, whatever their sense of humour.

Cyzicus and many of the Doliones came down from the city and thanked us for exterminating a long-standing threat. We shook hands all round, slapped each other's backs, said our farewells and weighed anchor. We were off again!

The sea was somewhat choppy, but there was a slight breeze from the south-east which carried us up the western flank of the island, but when we rounded its north-west corner and turned eastward, the breeze veered to an easterly and freshened. We had to row hard to make any headway. By evening we had passed the eastern tip of the island and headed south-east, hoping to hit the coast again before dark. However it was well past midnight before we found land and a suitable rock on the shore to which we could fasten our mooring ropes.

The night was dark and visibility was restricted to what little moonlight was not obscured by a thick layer of clouds. We disembarked and settled down to sleep on the beach. About three hours later, Zetes and Calais sounded the alarm.

We immediately armed ourselves and found ourselves facing the silhouettes of a large band of what appeared to be heavily armed warriors. I gave battle instructions to the crew, who arrayed themselves so that each one of us could engage with the enemy on a one-to-one basis.

We were not, apparently, heavily outnumbered and our superiority in heroic skills ensured that the engagement was soon over. The enemy retreated into the darkness leaving behind thirteen corpses. The Argonauts sustained only minor injuries which I treated as best I could by the light of a flickering torch. We were, of course, very weary after a long day of tough rowing and with our sleep interrupted by a short but sharp battle. We went back to sleep, while Zetes and Calais made frequent flights round about to try to ensure that we were not surprised by another attack.

Came the dawn, a dull, miserable, sultry dawn, the kind of dawn that makes men wish they were somewhere else. I awoke, cold and stiff, before any of the others, except for Zetes and Calais who had just returned from a brief flight of sentry duty and were resting on *Argo*'s prow.

"Have you any idea where we are?" I asked them.

"Surprise, surprise!" replied Zetes. "I think we are nearly back to where we left yesterday morning. The light is still dim, but I think I saw that isthmus near the city of Cyzicus about five miles away to our south-west along the coast of this island."

Calais continued: "That mountain inland to our north certainly looks like one of the peaks we saw to the east of Mount Dindymon. I reckon that the east wind last night blew us back westwards round the island when we thought we were making headway eastwards."

I had a nasty feeling that something was seriously wrong. I decided to inspect the corpses from the night's battle in order to ascertain what kind of foe we had encountered. The first corpse I came to belonged to the warrior I myself had killed. I remembered shattering his breast-bone with my spear. I removed his helmet and stared into his face which stared back at me with glazed eyes.

I turned and ran like a drunk into the sea and was sick.

The warrior I had killed was the king of the Doliones, King Cyzicus.

31

Sixteen days of grief

I stood there up to my waist in water, wanting desperately to drown myself. I glanced round once and saw the others wandering up and down the array of corpses, and letting out cries of alarm and grief from time to time. What was I, their captain, doing, standing in the sea and being sick, when my crew might need my leadership? Well, let them choose another captain if they wanted to. I was obviously a failure.

I felt a hand on my shoulder.

"Don't hurry it, dear boy. The others also need time to collect themselves together. When you feel better, and not till then, come back and tell us what to do, because we don't know. We need your leadership now as never before. And if you think there might be some other Argonaut who could take over from you and do the job better, forget it. There isn't one, except perhaps Peleus, and he would run a mile if you suggested it."

It was Argus. I took his advice and delayed for five minutes or so after he had returned to the shore. Then I waded back myself, stood on a the large rock to which *Argo* had been moored and addressed the crew:

"Fellow Argonauts, words cannot express our sorrow for this disaster, but our duty lies in helping our hosts of yesterday cope with their grief. We must pray to all the gods in Olympus to help us in this task. But what we must do immediately is to make stretchers for these corpses and carry them with dignity to the city of Cyzicus. When we get there, each one of you who killed one or more of these Doliones must make himself responsible for each victim and carry him to his home and share the grief of his family."

For the record, here is a list of who killed whom:

Acastus:	Sphodris
Castor:	Megalossaces
Clytius:	Hyacinthus
Heracles:	Telecles and Megabrontes
Idas:	Promeus
Jason:	Cyzicus
Meleager:	Itymoneus and Artaces
Peleus:	Zelys and Gephyrus
Polydeuces:	Phlogius
Telamon:	Basileus

The Doliones met us at the city gates. Words were few, except that they said they thought we had been an attacking force of Pelasgian Makrians, their neighbours and enemies. Argonauts who had not killed specific warriors were made welcome at the homes of the more fortunate. I stayed with the body of Cyzicus at the royal palace, but saw little of Cleite, his widow, who preferred to be alone with her grief in her bridal chambers.

For the next three days we joined the Doliones in grieving for their dead king, wailing and weeping and tearing our hair. On the third day the Doliones took Cyzicus's body to a level meadow where they marched three times round him in full ceremonial bronze armour and buried him in a tomb over which they raised a large barrow. They then held funeral games on the plain in accordance with their ancestral customs.

After the games I trudged wearily back to the palace, intending to request an audience with Cleite so that I could recount to her the dignity with which her people had performed her husband's funeral rites.

It was not to be. When I arrived at the steps before the palace gates, I was met by one of her maids who told me the terrible news.

"Queen Cleite has hanged herself," she said.

I sat down on the steps and buried my face in my hands. I was feeling desperate and tried to remember and make sense of what Argus had said to me three days before.

I must have been there over half an hour when I sensed the presence of somebody sitting on the steps near me. It was Peleus.

"What do you want?" I asked him irritably. "This is no time for frivolity."

"I'm not feeling frivolous," he said. "I've heard the dreadful news. When you have expressed your sympathies with the palace staff, perhaps you could help me out. As you will remember, I was unfortunate because I killed two of the Doliones, Zelys and Gephyrus. I have been trying to share their grief but dealing with two separate families is proving too much for me. Could you take on one of them from me, say, the family of Gephyrus, so that I can spend more time with the family of Zelys?"

I felt reproved and was tempted to lighten the conversation by suggesting that he had been accident-prone as usual, but I thought better of it.

"Of course I will," I replied. "Come to think of it, Heracles and Meleager both killed two of Doliones apiece. I must ask if they also need some help. It's very worrying that I didn't think of such an obvious problem before. I'm beginning to wonder if I'm the man for the job of captain."

"Rubbish," responded Peleus. "Strong emotion quite often banishes rational thought. I remember it well."

I laughed, remembering the cuttlefish and the sepia-coloured ink.

"Give me half an hour or so with the palace staff," I said, "and then perhaps you could show me the way to meet with the family of Gephyrus."

They proved to be a lovely family and they treated me like a prince and not a murderer. In fact, I stayed with them for the next twelve days. The weather was continuously foul, night and day, with a piercing east wind which prevented any hopes of our sailing onwards.

But on the night of the twelfth day, I had taken one night's leave of the family and had joined Acastus and Mopsus on sentry duty at the anchorage where we had left the *Argo*. Just before dawn Mopsus observed an halcyon bird hovering over my head (I was off-watch at the time, asleep and wrapped up warm in sheepskins). It suddenly rose up, as though disturbed by a god, veered away and settled on the stern-ornament of the *Argo*. Mopsus understood the language of birds, having been taught their language by Apollo himself, and was our soothsayer, second in importance to Idmon. He wasted no time in waking me, and told me what he had seen.

"Jason," he continued, "the message of the halcyon bird is clear. What we must do is climb Mount Dindymon to where, I believe, there is a sacred temple near its peak. There we must appease the great goddess Rhea, mother of Zeus, upon whose power the winds, the sea, all the earth below and the snowy seat of Olympus depend. It is said that when from the mountains she ascends the mighty heaven, even Zeus himself gives way. If we do this, these fiendish east winds will cease."

At last here were clear instructions on what must be done. I ran along the coast to the city and called an assembly of the heroes in the market square. I instructed ten of them to join Mopsus and Acastus at the *Argo* and row it to the harbour near the city on the eastern side of the isthmus. Four of the crew were to stay behind to guard the ship while the other eight were to join the rest of us later at the holy site on the mountain.

And so the remaining forty-three of us climbed up Mount Dindymon. We asked for the gift of two oxen which would be needed for the sacrifice when we got to the temple; these were given readily and we drove them before us up the mountain side. After several hours we reached its summit, something which we had failed to do when we were attacked by the six-armed monsters.

We were fortunate because the early morning mist had cleared and the distant hills and coastline were distinct. Lyncaeus (he was the Argonaut with the sharpest eye-sight I have ever experienced) said he could see the whole coastline to the east of us. He pointed out various rivers and plains to our west, Mount Mysius to our east-south-east and, most importantly, the entrance to the Bosporus to our north-east, through which we would presumably have to sail if we were to gain entrance to the Black Sea.

Mopsus, who had experience of such things, organised the ceremony. Argus located the massive trunk of an ancient vine which was growing in the forest which covered the side of the mountain. Heracles tore this from the ground and set it on an outcrop of rock beneath a canopy of lofty oak-trees. Argus then drew his trusty adze from the leather belt round his waist and skilfully shaped it to form the sacred image of the mountain goddess, and Mopsus ordered other heroes to build an altar of small stones nearby. We all then crowned our heads with oak-leaves. The oxen were sacrificed and I poured libations over the flames.

Unfortunately we could still hear the piercing cries of grief for their king and queen and lost warriors which came wafting up the mountain-side from the city of Cyzicus below us. These were in danger of casting an ill-omen over our ceremonial rites. Orpheus saved the situation by commanding the heroes to perform a dance to his music, clashing their swords on their shields to drown the noise from the city. (I understand this created a precedent for the ceremony in which the inhabitants of that land continued to appease the goddess Rhea with tambourines and drums.)

Our sacrifices were effective. The goddess was obviously pleased. Magic abounded: Trees began to teem with fruit; flower-buds suddenly bloomed in the grass; wild beasts from the forest left their lairs and came fawning on the heroes, swishing their tails. And, from beneath the rocky outcrop where Argus had fashioned the image of the goddess, a new spring of crystal-clear water gushed forth, and this on a mountain where no water had ever been seen before. (I believe the inhabitants of that land thereafter called it Jason's Spring, for which I feel very honoured!)

So we feasted well, sang Rhea's praises and got rather merry (the local wine was rather strong). It was dusk as we came back down off the mountain and spent our last night with our sorrowing hosts. At dawn they escorted us to the *Argo* which was lying in their eastern harbour and bade us farewell. The east wind had dropped completely and there was not a breath of wind stirring anywhere.

We rowed steadily out of the harbour, with our sail neatly furled in its buntlines. There was not a sound to be heard except the gentle splash and swish as the oars entered and left the water.

I glanced at our heroes and at our receding hosts. Most cheeks were glistening with tears.

32

Heracles breaks his oar

We rowed steadily for ten hours, following the southern coast of the Sea of Marmara, when I suddenly became impatient with our progress.

"Why don't we try manning all fifty oars for the rest of today?" I asked Tiphys. "The crew have had it easy physically for sixteen days, and we really must get on."

Tiphys looked dubious, but replied, "You're the captain. If that's what you want, that's what we must do."

And so the relief crew manned the idle ten oars, and we surged forward with all fifty oars pulling together. The crew sensed the exhilaration of speed and each one of them tried to rival the others. With a calm sea, we must have set some kind of speed record. It became a competition to see who could keep rowing the longest. Can you guess who won?

Heracles and Ancaeus, of course! These two kept pulling away mightily on their oars, and as the rest of the crew dropped out one by one from exhaustion, they cheered them on. I must admit that it was impressive to see just two oarsmen propelling a fifty-oared vessel without help from wind or current.

This was fine, of course, and good fun, until Ancaeus tired and stopped rowing. Then it took five of us on the quarterdeck straining at holding the steering oars, trying to keep the *Argo* on a straight course.

"That's enough, now, Heracles," I cried, but to no avail. He kept on pulling on his oar, with his strong arms sending great shudders throughout the ship. Even Argus started to look worried, when:

SNAP!

Heracles's oar was in two pieces; one floated away behind us, and the other remained in his hands as he fell crashing back on to the lap of the oarsman behind him. I can see it even now in my mind's eye, and it still brings a smile to my face.

The sea was beginning to get choppy from the evening breezes which come down the river valleys. I decided that enough was enough, and that we should make landfall. Mount Arganthonius loomed ahead of us and we dropped the anchor stone at the mouth of the Cianian estuary. We had heard from Cyzicus that the Mysians who occupied this section of coast might not be friendly, but this did not prove to be the case.

Quite the reverse in fact. We were made most welcome by a group of them and provided with plentiful supplies of sheep and wine. Heracles wandered off with Hylas to find himself a suitable tree to replace the oar he had broken. I organised a party to collect firewood, another to gather foliage for bedding and others to twirl firesticks, mix wine in our winebowls and otherwise prepare for the sacrifice that I planned for Apollo, the god of 'Happy Landings', and (of course) the feast to follow it.

After the feast, we all felt very weary and went to sleep almost immediately, except, of course for those on sentry duty.

While it was still dark, I felt my shoulder being shaken. It was Tiphys.

"What's wrong now?" I asked him, somewhat irritably. "I can see the morning star just over the top of the mountain. I thought we agreed we would wait at least for dawn before carrying on."

"Please yourself," he replied, "but can't you feel the breeze? It's a westerly, and we haven't felt one of those for very many days now. I think the crew would like a rest from rowing while we've got the chance."

"Too true, Tiphys," I said. "Wakey, wakey, everyone," I cried. "We're sailing NOW!"

Grumpiness was followed by gratitude as the crew climbed aboard, unfurled our sail, tightened the backstays, adjusted the port and starboard braces and hauled up the anchor stone. The wind bellied out the sail and we shot forward past Poseidon's promontory faster than could have been achieved by all fifty oars pulling in perfect partnership.

Several hours later, bright-eyed dawn lit up the eastern sky, and the hills to our south glistened with dew.

I counted fifty-two. What was wrong with me? I counted again. There were only fifty-two still.

"Tiphys," I cried in a panic, "there's only fifty-two!"

"Fifty-two what?"

"Argonauts, of course," I replied.

"Rubbish," he said. "I expect three of the relief crew are sleeping under the foredeck or aft under this quarterdeck here." He stamped his foot vigorously on the deck, but to no effect.

I sent someone to look, but nobody was there. "Who is missing?" I asked.

"Heracles...and Hylas...and Polyphemus," came the replies.

"It's all you fault," screamed Telamon, crowding over Tiphys. "If you hadn't rushed us on board in the middle of the night, we would never have left behind three of our most valued Argonauts, and particularly the mighty Heracles. We shall miss him sorely at his oar when we meet with the raging waters which flow from the Black Sea. I insist that we go back for all three of them."

Then turning to me, he said, "If it was not possible to count us on land in the darkness, you should have counted us as we climbed on board or got Lyncaeus to do it for you. In fact, I suspect you left Heracles behind deliberately, to stop his fame eclipsing your own—always assuming, of course, that we do ever get back home without his strength to help us."

With difficulty I kept my cool. I replied, "I'm as sorry as you are that we have left three of the crew behind, but it would mean rowing hard against this westerly to retrace our steps now. In any case, perhaps Heracles is rather too strong an oarsman. I will consider the matter soon and let you know my decision. In the meantime, may I remind you that you are not in a position to insist on anything."

Peleus came up. I expected him to be annoyed with me for putting his brother in his place, but all he whispered in my ear was: "I been longing for ages to talk to him like that. Thanks!"

But my decision was made for me. We heard shouts from Zetes and Calais, who were circling aloft, for us to look down into the sea on the port side. And there we saw Glaucus, the wise and eloquent spokesman of the sea-god Nereus, emerging from the salt-depths. He raised his shaggy head and torso from the sea as far as his waist, clutched the stern-post of *Argo* and addressed us:

"Hold on, you hot-heads! Are you not afraid of going against destiny—the will of mighty Zeus himself? It is the fate of Heracles to labour for insolent Eurystheus and to accomplish all twelve labours and then dwell with the immortals. Likewise Polyphemus is fated to found the glorious city of Cius at the head of the estuary you have just left behind. And as for Hylas, you would never find him. A goddess-nymph has claimed him for her husband, and it was in searching for him that the other two were delayed. Even if you did return for them, they would not come with you. Waste no more time in advancing your adventure."

Suddenly he plunged beneath the waves and all we could see were dark eddies and seething foam dashing against the side of *Argo* as it flew through the sea.

So that was that. The heroes were satisfied and resumed resting as the wind carried us along before it. Telamon came up and apologised to Tiphys and me.

"Forget it," I said. "I myself was in a tricky mood yesterday and almost let Heracles harm our ship. We may officially be heroes, but we're all only human at heart."

"Well, most of us are," he responded, "at any rate in some respects," while looking in the direction of Zetes and Calais who were flying around ahead of us, keeping a look-out for dangerous shallows.

All that day and through the following night *Argo* flew in front of a stiff southerly breeze. We were heading, we hoped, towards the entrance to the Bosporus. Then at daybreak, the breeze dropped. We saw land ahead and a wide bay. Needing sleep, we rowed the ship towards it and ran her ashore on the beach. We were hoping for a welcome from any natives of the area.

We were disappointed.

33

What had happened to Heracles?

Here in the Elysian Fields, it is easy to look back and understand better those things which were hidden from us while living. For example, we had received a brief report from Glaucus, the wise and eloquent spokesman of the sea-god Nereus, concerning the reasons why Heracles, Hylas and Polyphemus had failed to return to our camp before Tiphys suggested our sudden departure.

For the record, here is what happened. (I obtained this information direct from the heroes themselves here in the Fields.)

Hylas, who was Heracles's squire, knew that his lord had gone into the forest looking for a tree suitable for a replacement oar. So he thought he would do something useful by looking for a plentiful supply of pure spring water ready for the evening feast and in preparation for his lord's return. He took with him a pitcher of bronze, and soon came to a spring which the local inhabitants called *Pegai* or *The Springs*. It so happened that the nymphs of the spring were just beginning their dance there, because it was the custom of all the nymphs who haunted that lovely headland to honour the great goddess Artemis with their songs. Nymphs had gathered there from all the mountain peaks and glades from far around. But one particular nymph was, at that moment, rising from out of that fair-flowing spring, when she perceived Hylas close at hand. The full moon was casting its silvery glow around his head and torso, stunning her senses. She could not resist him. As soon as he dipped his pitcher in the stream, straightway she clasped her left arm above his neck and with her right arm drew down his elbow, plunging him into the depths of her home.

Hylas said he never knew how long he dwelt with her, until he was allowed here. However, he said the experience was very pleasant, somewhat like the Elysian Fields, though rather more watery.

Polyphemus had been married to Laonome, who was Heracles's sister. He was one of the Lapiths and in his youth had fought with them in their war against the centaurs. He was now no longer young, but was still a warrior to be respected.

He was one of the party which I had deputed to gather firewood. He said that he wanted to see how his brother-in-law set about tearing up a tree suitable for a replacement oar, so he wandered off from the others but failed to find Heracles. He was about to give up and try to join the other wood-gatherers when he heard Hylas cry out in terror. Suspecting that Hylas had been attacked by some wild beast or perhaps ambushed by hostile natives, he rushed, sword in hand, to the place where he thought the cry had come from, but found nothing. He wandered round and round the spring he found there, slashing away at the undergrowth with his sword, until, in the moonlight, he saw Heracles returning from the forest with a massive but slender pine tree, roots and all, in his hand.

"Dreadful news, Heracles," he cried. "I heard Hylas cry out in terror, and I fear he has been carried off by some beasts or brigands. I have searched everywhere round here, but have found nothing."

Polyphemus went on to describe the terrible anguish of Heracles, who had lost not only his squire but the friend whom he loved more than anyone. Sweat poured from his temples and his blood seemed to boil within him. He dropped the pine-tree and stampeded off bellowing like a bull stung by a gadfly.

This went on for days until even Heracles had to stop for a rest. Then, Polyphemus said, they returned to the shore, but the *Argo* had gone. Heracles eventually wandered off disconsolate, presumably to continue with his labours, while he, Polyphemus, settled with the native Mysians of the region and in due course founded the city of Cius (today's Gemlik) where the River Cius flows out into the Cianian gulf.

I have often been tempted to ask Heracles for his account, but have not dared. I understand that he was furious at being left behind. I think this was rather unreasonable of him, but understandable in the circumstances. In any case, there would be little that he could add to Polyphemus's account.

However, leave the three of them behind we did, for better or for worse, and, having run before a breeze all night, we had run *Argo* ashore.

As I said at the end of the last chapter, we were hoping for a welcome from any natives of the area, but we were disappointed.

34

Amycus, king of the Bebryces

We had nearly unpacked the stores necessary for our breakfast when Zetes and Calais, who had been performing a reconnaissance of the surrounding area, flew in with a report.

"There may be trouble ahead," said Zetes.

"And here it comes now," continued Calais, as a band of natives came swaggering down on to the beach, led by an enormous piece of barbarity.

"And who may you be?" I asked him.

He glared at me with a look which could be insufficiently described as disdainful.

"I am Amycus," he replied, "son of the Bithynian nymph Melie and the god Poseidon, who created and who protects the great Bebrycians, some of whom you see with me here. I am their king."

"And," I replied, "I am J…"

"I do not care who you are," Amycus interrupted, "but hear you this:

"Any foreigner who enters my realm is prohibited from leaving until he has fought me in a boxing match. You will therefore choose one of your motley crew to fight me now. The rest of you will sit down and remain seated until I have finished with him.

"Resistance is useless."

You can imagine the effect that this effrontery had on my crew of the noblest heroes of the known world. They were about to set about these insolent Bebrycians and were only waiting for a word from me to do so.

But Polydeuces, the twin brother of Castor, came forward immediately. He was, of course, renowned as a champion boxer. He strode up to Amycus and spoke to him softly:

"I'll take you on, whoever you are, in spite of your arrogant rudeness."

Amycus was obviously upset by such a calm response.

His eyes rolled round in his purple face, and he glared at Polydeuces with huge hatred.

They agreed on a level spot for the fight. A henchman of Amycus came forward with two pairs of boxing gloves which he placed on the ground in front of the contestants. These gloves were made of raw hide, oven-dry and as hard as bronze.

"Choose your gloves," growled Amycus, "and get your seconds to put them on for you." Our mighty Talaus came forward with Castor and they bound the gloves carefully on Polydeuces's hands, giving him calm words of encouragement. Amycus's henchmen put his gloves on, but omitted the words of encouragement, which they obviously considered inappropriate.

Both sides of spectators sat down opposite each other round the perimeter of the rink. The Bebrycians had seen these fights many times before, and were grinning in anticipation of a quick and bloody victory for their king, before attacking and overwhelming us. We, in our turn, were confident that our experience and prowess would be equal to any challenge.

The boxers raised their hands in front of their faces. Amycus rushed forward with arms flailing left and right, but Polydeuces took stock of his weak and strong points, parried his rushes and traded punch for punch.

After three minutes, which seemed like seven, they drew apart to gather their breath. Then Amycus rushed forward and suddenly raised both his hands to bring them crashing down on his opponent's skull. Polydeuces swerved to his left, then immediately to his right, causing Amycus to lose the accuracy of his aim. His fists came crashing down

Polydeuces's left arm, skinning off its flesh. But, simultaneously, Polydeuces swung his right arm round like a streak of lightning and speared his rawhide glove into Amycus's head, just behind its left ear, smashing the bones of the skull with a force that even Heracles with his club could scarcely have equalled.

Amycus shuddered, collapsed and died.

There followed a stunned silence as the Bebrycians came to terms with a completely unexpected outcome to the fight. Then, at a signal from Amycus's chief henchman, they picked up their clubs and spears and rushed at Polydeuces.

Fortunately I had anticipated what would happen when Polydeuces won and had instructed Castor to protect his brother and the other heroes to mark their opposite numbers. By some strange coincidence, each side now numbered fifty-two in number with the death of Amycus. But the battle was by no means a walk-over for us. The enemy fought with a ferocity which matched that once flaunted by their dead king, and we sustained many wounds.

Talaus, one of my relations, was wounded by a great bully of a Bebrycian, when his bronze spear hit him, but Talaus had a lucky escape: the spear cut right through his leather belt but only grazed his skin. Iphitus also was injured. (Incidentally, this Iphitus was the son of Eurytus and brother of Clytius, another Argonaut, both of whom came from Euboea. Eurytus, their father, was an archer who was renowned for his skill with the bow, and he once made the mistake of challenging Apollo who slew him for his presumption. His great bow was inherited by Iphitus who later gave it to Odysseus, who used it to slay the suitors of his wife Penelope. But that is another story.) Iphitus, while busy killing Bebrycians with his great bow, was struck by the great club of a Bebrycian named Aretus, but Aretus in turn was struck down by the sharp sword of Clytius.

There were a large number of fatalities on the Bebrycian side. Castor struck the head of a warrior with such a downward force that the severed halves fell down each side of his shoulders. Polydeuces killed another two: he winded the first with a running kick and punched the second so hard above his left eye that the eyelid was torn off and the eyeball exposed; each injury resulted in instant death.

When I sensed that we were winning the battle, I called upon Peleus, his brother Telamon together with Ancaeus, who, you may remember, was the outsize Argonaut who had rowed opposite Heracles and came to us from Arcadia brandishing a huge two-edged axe in his right hand and dressed in a bearskin from a bear he had caught on Mount Maenalus. The four of us made a final combined onslaught on the remaining enemy warriors. We felt like a band of beekeepers smoking out a swarm of bees. We killed seventeen of them before the rest retreated in panic and scattered in the direction of the hills.

35

We meet a Mariandynian

We chased them inland until we came to their vineyards and villages, where we stopped while their warriors disappeared into the hills beyond. The reason we stopped was because their houses and crops had obviously been very recently ravaged, presumably while we engaged in battle on the beach, and we were interested to find out why.

We came across a lone stranger sitting in front of a tavern drinking some wine and obviously enjoying it.

"Hi there!" he welcomed us. "I am glad that your battle went off well. On behalf of King Lycus and the Mariandyni of whom I am proud to be one, thank you very much for doing what we had planned to do ourselves."

"Tell us more," I demanded.

"Well, we live along the coast from here, about seventy-five miles away, and we have been getting rather tired of the aggressive behaviour of Amycus and his Bebrycian brigands. We have only to stray into their territory to be challenged to one of Amycus's ridiculous boxing matches, because he always wins, and then his mates try to finish us off as well. Well, enough was enough, so we set out on our horses yesterday intending to finish them all off once and for all, or at least to kill Amycus and deplete their numbers to a level that would present no threat for the foreseeable future. But when we arrived, we watched you from afar and saw that you not only killed Amycus, but killed a dozen or so of their number before starting to rout the rest of them."

"Actually," I interrupted, "we killed seventeen besides Amycus."

"Anyway," he continued, pretending not to have heard me, "our King Lycus did not want to hang around here, since he did not know your nature or intentions, friendly or otherwise, and, since his objectives had been achieved, he left me behind to explain things to you, with the hope, he said for me, that you would not kill me. He also asked me to invite you all to call in at his palace, if ever you were passing that way. He would like to meet such a magnificent band of warriors, to thank you and congratulate you for your prowess today over such a rude rabble of ruffians. However, he suggests you travel to see us by land, since the sea voyage into the Black Sea is fraught with problems and possible impossibilities. Sorry, I've been talking too much as usual. Any questions?"

I explained to him who we were and what we expected to achieve, and I asked him to convey this information to his king.

"However," I continued, "can you tell me why the sea journey into the Black Sea is so difficult? We really need to know."

"I believe," he replied, "that the trouble is not only with the swift currents pouring from the Black Sea down the Bosporus into the Sea of Marmora, but with the actual exit from the Bosporus into the Black Sea. They say that there are rocks there which are unstable, and crush any vessel attempting to make a passage in either direction. That's why we always travel by land, except of course for sailing within the Black Sea itself, and even then we try to keep as close to the south coast as possible."

"Somehow or other," I responded, "we have got to sail through the Bosporus and into the Black Sea. We are hoping to get some guidance from a prophet who, we have heard, lives somewhere on the opposite shore."

"That will be Phineus, no doubt," he replied, "and the best of luck."

"By the way," he went on, "we have taken most of their animals and valuables with us, but king Lycus said to leave enough sheep and a few cattle and other provisions for your continuing journey."

"Thank you very much; very kind of you," I said.

"Don't mention it," he replied. "I'd better be getting back home as far as possible before dark. Oh, and don't forget the invite when, or rather if, you're passing."

He whistled for his horse, which appeared from grazing in the garden of the tavern; he jumped on it and galloped off.

"Strange man," commented Peleus, as I bandaged his foot (he had stepped on a sharp shell back on the beach) and treated many of the others for their wounds. Talaus's wound was nasty but some of Cheiron's ointment did the trick. Iphitus had an enormous multi-coloured bruise developing, which the others crowded round to admire, but a calendula-based salve spoilt the effect.

We returned to the shore and decided to have a great feast with gallons of wine and blazing sacrifices of the animals from the Bebrycian villages. The *Argo* had been tied to a laurel tree and we used the leaves from this tree to adorn our heads. We sang songs in praise of Polydeuces, accompanied by the melodious music of Orpheus. We enjoyed ourselves and felt we deserved it.

The other fifty-one Argonauts slept soundly, but my sleep was fitful. I suppose I was worried about the next stage of our adventure.

36

We meet with Phineus

As soon as dawn crawled yellow-robed from Ocean's streams far beyond the eastern hills, I stirred the fifty-one others from their stentorian slumbers.

"Wakey, wakey!" I cried. "Let's get on with it while the winds are favourable for our passage into the Bosporus."

We stowed in the *Argo* as much booty as Argus said we could safely carry, and this even included seven sheep from the Bebrycian flocks, as well as much wine and meat left over from the previous night's feast. We loosed the ropes from the laurel tree and headed north-west for the entrance to the Bosporus.

By early afternoon we had turned north-east into its swirling waters. A strong wind filled our sails, and Tiphys had insisted on all fifty oars being manned. This meant Zetes, Calais and Orpheus taking a turn at rowing, which they did with good grace. We certainly needed both sail- and oar-power against the strong and turbulent current pouring down that channel between Europe and Asia.

And then, looking ahead, I saw what looked like a mountain rushing down the channel towards us. Tiphys saw it too. Luckily the rest of the crew (all fifty of them at their oars) could not see it, or they might have panicked. Of course it was not a mountain; it was a gigantic wave bearing down on us. I honestly thought we were done for. In no time at all, so it seemed, the wave towered above us, and I was waiting for it to crash down on the *Argo* and smash her into oblivion.

I looked at Tiphys. His face was white but he kept his cool.

"Hold this oar like this," he commanded me. "I'll deal with t'other." (*Argo* had two steering oars, one port, one starboard.) Immediately he snapped crisp commands to the oarsmen, which they obeyed instantly. Then we were soaring up the side of the mountain, then hovering precariously at the top, then slithering down the other side at a speed which I suspected *Argo* would never again exceed in her lifetime.

"Keep rowing," shouted Tiphys when more than a few Argonauts started to applaud his magnificent performance, and row they did. He was in no mood for sentimentality.

He steered for the nearest practical landfall on our port (i.e. the European) side of the Bosporus.

"I think you will agree," he said to me, "that we've had enough for today. Tomorrow I'll manoeuvre carefully northwards, probably hugging the coasts to avoid the strongest currents, and see if we can find where the prophet Phineus, son of Agenor, lives. It's somewhere along here, I believe. Both Idmon and Mopsus told me yesterday that we might find it advantageous to have a chat with him, if we can find him."

I agreed, of course. My respect for Tiphys's skill and judgement were at an all-time high. We anchored near a convenient beach and went through our usual routine in preparation for our night's sleep.

Peleus had a chat with me after we had sacrificed to

Poseidon (praying for a less hazardous sea-trip tomorrow) and wined and dined.

"That was a good performance from you and Tiphys," he said, tactfully including me in his praise. "I wondered what on earth (or should I say sea?) was happening when we started ascending up that wave. I didn't dare look round to see what was happening. Not that I had time to, what with following Tiphys's rapid-fire commands. How he got us over before we got swamped I'll never know. Anyway, well done, and all that!"

"Thanks," I replied. "But we'd better get some sleep, now," and I wished him goodnight.

Next day, under Tiphys's skilful navigation, with a good southerly wind behind us and with all fifty oars at work, we inched our way up the Bosporus. Tiphys expertly detected the occasional counter-currents to ease our battle against the main current, which was strong and flowing against us. This meant that we had to cross and recross the main channel from time to time, crawling sometimes up one side for several furlongs and then crossing the main stream to get back to the other side in order to take advantage of the counter-current there.

At last, in the middle of the afternoon, when we had changed once again to the European side of the channel, Tiphys peered at the coast on that side and said:

"I think that must be Phineus's walls. Look, over there! Can you see the remains of a small palace-like building with no roof, look, over there on the hillside. That must be it!"

"Right," I said. "Let's land there on the beach in that little bay."

We drew *Argo* on to the beach, and secured her to a convenient tree. I inspected the crew for tidiness and then arranged them in an orderly fashion before we walked quietly up the hillside, not wanting to alarm Phineus by an aggressive approach.

When we got to the ruined open-air palace, we could see a long table down the middle of the large single room, in the corner of which was a small roofed shelter, which Phineus presumably used to protect himself from the elements.

"Hello, there," I said with a loud voice. "Is anyone at home?"

A voice came from the shelter: "Not today, but thank you all the same!"

37

Phineus tells his story

Phineus's answer rather took me aback.

"We are the Argonauts, from Iolcos," I replied, "questing the Golden Fleece of Phrixus."

"That is different," replied the voice, and a shambling figure emerged from the shelter and staggered towards us, supported by a staff. His limbs shook with the weakness of old age, his shrivelled flesh was caked with dirt and his bones looked as though they were only held together by his skin.

I pulled a chair out from the table and helped him to sit down on it.

"Sorry I didn't recognise you immediately," he said, "but I presumed you were from the town trying to sell me rubbish in return for my short-term and long-term weather forecasts. I'm a prophet, you know, and the farmers find them useful."

"I'm not surprised," I replied. "Perhaps you could let us have one before we continue on our journey."

"Of course, I will, young Jason," he said. "At least, I presume you are Jason. I'm partially blind, you know, and one man looks very much like another to me. Sorry to be in such a state, but things are somewhat difficult for me at the moment, and I hope you are going to help me, if the oracle is correct. Perhaps you would like me to explain?"

"Please do," I replied, "but would it be all right if my fifty-one companions came in and sat down round your table. We've been rowing all day, and a rest would be welcome."

"Oh I'm so sorry," he said, "I'm getting so absent minded these days. Please do come in, all of you, but I'm afraid there's no food I can give you. It's all gone, and when I do get some more this afternoon, it will all go.

"Oh dear.... Oh dear, oh dear.... Oh dear, oh dear, oh dear."

"Please don't upset yourself," I replied. "We've brought our own food with us, and if there is anything we can do to help you, please let us know, and we'll do our best."

"Bless you," he replied. "Please be patient and I'll try to explain."

"Before you do," I said, "would you like something to eat from what we have brought with us?"

"Better not," he replied, "looking warily up at the skies. The moment I put any food to my lips, the Harpies swoop down and snatch it.

"You see, I am Phineus, son of Agenor, and years ago I was famous for my wealth and powers of prophesy. Somehow or other I upset Zeus because apparently I overstepped the mark in revealing the plans of the gods to mortal men, and did he make me suffer? Well you can see for yourself! Here I am, living in an open-air palace, nearly blind and almost starved to death!

"Those damned Harpies! Some call them the hounds of Zeus, but they are brutal birds with the speed of the swiftest winds who instantly appear from the sky and snatch any food I try to put to my lips.

"So, you may well ask, why am I not dead from starvation?"

He paused with eyebrows raised, and stared into my eyes, obviously not intending to continue until I had asked him:

"You poor old man, and why have the Harpies failed to starve you to death?"

"Not so much of the *old man*, if you please," he replied. "Well, they always leave me a few scraps, but these are fouled by the Harpies so that they stink horribly and taste foul. But I have to eat them just to keep body and soul together.

"But here's the good news: the oracle has revealed to me that when the *Argo* arrives here on its quest for the Golden Fleece, it will bring in its crew the two sons of the North Wind who alone have the ability to chase the Harpies away from these shores forever, and allow me to live out my days with at least some pleasure from nourishment.

"Pray tell me, are those two sons of Boreas indeed with you here?"

"Indeed they are," I replied, with some pleasure, and I called upon Zetes and Calais to come forward.

Zetes was the first to speak; he usually was the first, perhaps because Calais tended to be rather shy.

"Hi there, Phineus!" he said. "Very pleased to meet you, and very flattered to hear you say that only my brother and I can help you by chasing away those dreadful Harpies. But I hope you will not mind me saying this, but, will it not be somewhat dangerous for us to try to interfere with the will of Zeus? After all, the Harpies are his own personal hounds, and, swift as we are in flight, we would find it difficult, if not impossible, to avoid one of Zeus's thunderbolts."

Phineus looked rather annoyed.

"Listen here, young Zetes," he said. "I am Phineus, and a great prophet, instructed as I was by Apollo himself! And I swear, most solemnly, by Apollo and by the gods of the Underworld, and may they for ever haunt me in death if I die so perjured, that you will not incur the wrath of the gods if you help me as the oracle has said you would. Will that do?"

"Of course, and we are sorry we doubted your word, aren't we, dear Calais?"

"Yes, of course," said Calais.

At that moment, a stranger from the near-by town walked in with a barrow-load of provisions for Phineus.

"Hi there, Phineus!" he said. "Your weather forecast yesterday was spot-on. Good southerly wind and pressure rising. How about today?"

"More of the same," said Phineus, "and please meet some friends of mine, from Iolcos in Magnesia, on their way to claim the Golden Fleece back from King Aeetes in Colchis."

"Pleased to meet you," said the stranger. "Rather you than me. Can't you do anything about these wretched birds who keep snatching and fouling all the lovely food here that we keep bringing for Phineus?"

"We have the matter in hand," I replied. "No problem!"

"Good show! Well done, there! See you later!" and off he walked back towards the town.

"Who was that?" I asked Phineus.

"I forget now," he replied, "but he comes quite often."

"But I'd better try," he continued, "to eat some of this lovely food, before the Harpies see it!"

Whereupon he picked up an apple which was immediately snatched from his hand by one of the Harpies who appeared instantly from nowhere. There was a whole flock of them, huge inky-black birds of prey with evil eyes and twitching talons, snatching at the food on the table until only a few pathetic and putrid morsels were left.

But Zetes and Calais had immediately climbed on to the table and were slashing around with their swords. The birds were too quick for them, but soon zoomed upwards with the sons of Boreas flying after them in close pursuit.

It was all over in less than a minute, and the silence which followed was uncanny.

Phineus spoke first: "What did I tell you? I wasn't exaggerating, was I? And look at my table. How would you like to eat those stinking crumbs? I ask you…"

"Phineus," I said, "for heaven's sake, shut up, and let us give your table a good spring-clean and then we will

179

have a real feast, because we have with us in the good ship *Argo* much booty which we took on board after we had killed Amycus and defeated the Bebrycians. Somehow I do not think you will be troubled by those wretched Harpies again. "

For the first time, I saw Phineus begin to show the glimmerings of a smile, then break out into raucous laughter. It was a joy to see and hear him. It would be some time before his flesh supported his skin more adequately, but the future seemed bright for him at last.

While the other forty-eight Argonauts got to work fetching stores from the *Argo* and cleaning up Phineus's palace, Peleus and I had a brief chat.

"That was quite exciting, wasn't it?" said Peleus.

"Certainly was," I replied. "How long do you think Zetes and Calais will be gone? They may have to chase the Harpies all the way to their home in Crete, but that shouldn't take them too long, flying at that speed. Do you think they will be able to keep up with them? They are both quite fast but the Harpies seemed to fly at the speed of winds. Do you think that Phineus is to be believed when he says that Zeus will not harm them? In any case, I doubt if they will be back before we start our feast this evening. Perhaps they may not be back even before dawn. However, they are quite experienced at night flying, and the sky is not at all cloudy at present. What do you think?"

"Pass," he said. "How many Harpies were there then?"

"Seventeen," I replied, and we both joined in the preparations for our evening meal.

38

Phineus gives his prophesy

Seldom have I seen a man enjoy his food so much. Phineus tucked into his lamb chops as though there would be no tomorrow, though I noticed that he occasionally squinted up at the sky as though he half-expected the dreaded Harpies to reappear.

I must confess I was a little worried for Zetes and Calais. Peleus was sitting opposite me at the table and when he saw me looking anxious, he said:

"I bet you're wondering when those sons of Boreas will be getting back. So why don't you ask Phineus?"

"No need to," said Phineus, who was sitting next to me.

"And I am not deaf," he continued. "They'll get back here about dawn, dying to tell you all about it."

"Thank you for putting my mind at rest," I said. "But now that we've just about eaten all we want, and can look forward to enjoying some more of this excellent wine before we retire to sleep for the night, I wonder if you would be kind enough to advise us concerning our future adventures. You see, we know that, to get to Colchis where the Golden Fleece is in the custody of king Aeetes, we have somehow to sail into and across the Black Sea. But we have no map, and the journey, for all we know, may include many perils. So any help you can give us would be very welcome."

Phineus did not reply for some time, but sat slumped

back in his chair, sipping his wine and looking thoughtful. Eventually he spoke:

"You will appreciate that I have to be very careful. If I say too little, I shall be accused of being a rotten prophet. If I say too much, Zeus may send me something even worse than those dreadful Harpies, and I don't think I could stomach that. You see, what I am supposed to tell you is the whole truth so that you don't quite understand it. Do you understand?"

"Not quite," I replied.

"Well, that's all right then," he continued. "So here goes:

"When you sail from here, you will be travelling north against some of the strongest currents in the world. Many rivers run into the Black Sea, and all its waters have eventually to pass down the Bosporus into the Sea of Marmara before emerging into the Aegean Sea. Even with fifty oars and fifty heroes pulling them, you will still need a good southerly wind behind you to make any headway. So you will be ill-advised to try a passage until the Etesian winds which are now upon us have ceased.

"And there is a further hazard. At the northern exit from the Bosporus, at the end of the straits, are the Clashing Rocks—the Symplegades. These are very unstable and the seas knock them this way and that, and, as far as I know, no ship has ever passed between them without being crushed to splinters and all hands lost. Occasionally they even stick together making the seas behind them to build up mightily. Then suddenly, without warning, they spring apart, sending a mountain of water towering down the straits and crushing any vessel in its path."

"I know," I interrupted. "The good ship *Argo* climbed

over one of these mountains yesterday, steered by our genius helmsman, Tiphys, whom you see over there."

"No I don't," responded Phineus, "but please, Tiphys, accept my congratulations. This bodes well for your next hurdle: getting *Argo* through the Clashing Rocks themselves. Of course, you may not be able to do it, in which case, hard luck!

"But listen carefully, and take my advice. As you approach those fearsome cliffs, send out a dove to see if she can get through without getting squashed. If she does, then immediately, before the rocks have had time to crash together again, put on full fifty-oar power and pray that you get through. But if the dove fails to make it, I advise you to abandon the whole expedition. I know that you all would be ashamed to return home and admit defeat, but at least, you would all be alive, and perhaps be able to plan a land-based expedition to retrieve the Fleece."

You could have heard a feather fall. Tiphys spoke for all of us.

"We would rather die in the attempt than abandon our venture," he said.

Phineus grew angry. "Do you dare to ignore the advice of Apollo, whose prophet I am? Do you think you know better than the gods themselves? Thank you for saving me from the Harpies, but you can leave now if you want, and to hell with the lot of you!"

"Please, please, please, forgive us," I said. "It's simply that it will be extremely hard for us, as heroes, to abandon our quest, for which we have received so many good omens from the gods."

"I'm sorry I lost my temper," said Phineus. "Being

inspired by a god is sometimes a highly emotional experience. Well, let's hope the dove gets through."

"If she does," he continued, "and you all follow through safely, I, for one, shall be very pleased. Because the oracle says that if you do, then the Clashing Rocks will clash no more, and remain open for all ships to pass in safety for ever more."

"In that case," I said, "we should be doing mankind a great favour by enabling a permanent passage for ships between the two great seas, the Black and the Aegean. Also it will make returning home from Colchis a relative doddle, especially with the currents in our favour."

"Do you want to hear the rest of my prophesy or not?" said Phineus.

"I'm so sorry," I said. "Of course we do. Please continue, and I'll not interrupt again."

"Very well," said Phineus. "Assuming that you do get through the Symplegades unscathed, and that's a big assumption, I can help you by describing the south coast of the Black Sea, which you will be well advised to stick to like a limpet. If you try to sail across the sea direct to Colchis, which is on the east coast of the Sea, you will be asking for trouble. The winds and the currents can be very treacherous."

Phineus then went on to describe in detail the bays, the beaches and the promontories, the rivers which flow into the Sea, and the various tribes of men who inhabit the lands along its great south coast. Of course, I wished that I could have made notes as he spoke, but fortunately my training in Cheiron's School enabled me to visualise the coast as though I was flying above it and thus to create a mental map as Phineus unfolded his description.

"But I have two pieces of advice to give you," he said as his prophesy drew to its close.

"First, do not neglect to land on a rather inhospitable island known as the Isle of Ares. This will not be easy, since it is protected by a large number of rather fierce birds, and you will have to find some means of protecting yourselves against them. Incidentally, there is a stone altar there which was built by two queens of the Amazons while they were on some campaign or other."

"Why are you advising us to land on this island?" I asked him.

"Because I now regard you as a friend," he replied.

"That's not quite what I meant," I said. "Why…?"

"Secondly," he interrupted with a sigh, "when you arrive at the farthest corner of the Black Sea, you will see some distant mountains where are the origins of the River Phasis which flows into the Sea there. Row the *Argo* quietly into the marshes at its mouth, and you will see the lofty walls of the great city of King Aeetes, and the gloomy grove of Ares, within which lies an oak on the top of which is spread the Golden Fleece, protected by a formidable serpent which never sleeps but casts its unblinking eyes in all directions continuously, day and night."

We waited for several minutes, expecting Phineus to continue, but he did not. Perhaps he was tired.

"That sounds all very terrifying," I said eventually. "But can you please tell us, what we are to do then? And if we do succeed in obtaining the Fleece, how are we to return home? Do we simply follow the course you have outlined to us to get there, or would it be advisable to find a different route? After all, this is all new and strange to us, and we have no idea of what further perils may lie before us."

"I can tell you no more," Phineus replied, "except that you would be well advised to put your trust in the gods, particularly Aphrodite."

"Why Aphrodite?" I asked.

Phineus smiled. "Just believe me," he said, "but I can say no more. I would now like to go to bed. It's been a long and rather tiring day, though I must say it's wonderful to be rid of those dreadful Harpies at long last, and to enjoy an excellent meal for a change. Thank you and goodnight."

And off he went to bed in his little shelter in the corner of the open-air room of the ruined palace.

39

The Etesian Winds

I slept fitfully, with intermittent dreams arising, no doubt, from the long prophesy of Phineus. Sometimes we were sailing backwards, chased by the many fierce tribes that Phineus had listed, at other times we were being dive-bombed by the birds of Ares.

I was woken up at dawn by a flapping of wings above my head, and this proved to be the sons of Boreas returning from their long flight.

"Glad to see you back safe and sound," I said.

All the other Argonauts were now wide awake and demanding to hear an account of what had happened to the Harpies.

Zetes and Calais rested their feet on the back of some vacant chairs and Zetes asked Calais to start.

"You first," said Calais.

"Very well then," said Zetes. "Somehow or other, and we suspect it was Zeus who gave us the extra strength, we managed to keep up with the Harpies as they sped over the Sea of Marmara, down the Hellespont and into the Aegean. However, try as we might, our swords kept missing them despite all our efforts to make contact with them. Then, just as we felt we were going to catch up with them over the Floating Islands, we ran slap into a rainbow, down which the goddess Iris slithered and addressed us.

"'Hold it, you two,' she cried. 'Not so fast, there! The Harpies are the hounds of Zeus himself, his own personal pets, and he's asked me to say that you've done enough now. He thinks Phineus has suffered sufficient punishment for his indiscretions. He's asked me to give you my own personal pledge, by the waters of Styx, which to all the gods is the most dread and the most awesome, that the Harpies will never again trouble Phineus, and will stay in their home in their hiding-place on the island of Crete. Incidentally, these *Floating Islands* below us are hereby renamed the *Islands of Turning*, because here is where you will do your Turning and fly back to rejoin the Argonauts. I think that's all. Cheerio, and have a safe trip!' and Iris slithered back up her rainbow.

"We watched the Harpies disappear southwards towards Crete, and we turned to fly back here. However, as the rainbow faded, we received a thorough drenching from a squally shower. Whether it was because of this, or because Zeus withdrew the extra zest with which he had favoured us for the outward journey, or because a strong north-west wind seems to have developed overnight, anyway, whatever the reason, it took us the rest of the night to get back here. And please can we now get some shut-eye, because we're both feeling shattered, aren't we, Calais?"

"Yes," said Calais. "We are."

"Well done, both of you," I said. "You must both have a bite to eat, and have a good day's sleep."

All the Argonauts cheered them, and Phineus came to the door of his shelter and joined in.

So we all had breakfast, after which I turned to Phineus and said:

"I think that, once the sons of Boreas have had a rest, we must resume our journey without further delay. The sooner we attempt to pass the Clashing Rocks, the better."

"You must be joking," said Phineus.

"How do you mean?" I asked.

"Didn't you hear what those two bird-men said? The winds have changed to north-westerlies, and you'll need some good southerlies to get you through the Symplegades. Haven't you heard of the Etesian Winds? Didn't you learn anything at Cheiron's School?"

Peleus, who was sitting on the other side of the table, interrupted.

"Yes, of course," he said. "We did Etesian Winds in Mythology, didn't we, Jason?"

"We did indeed," I said, and then, thinking to call his bluff, I asked him, "Why don't you remind us all of the story?"

"Well," he said, with a grin, "there was this shepherdess, called Cyrene. One day she was looking after her flock of sheep when Apollo happened to be passing by, and he took a fancy to her, and whisked her off to Libya, where she bore him a son called Aristaeus. Apollo, in gratitude, made her a nymph and huntress and gave her the gift of longevity. But he took Aristaeus off to Cheiron's School where he was educated. Of course he was an old boy of the school while we were there, but Cheiron told us that, since leaving school, he had become an expert in Medicine and Prophesy, as well as a professional shepherd; I believe he had flocks all over Phthia and thereabouts.

"Later on he migrated to the island of Ceos, at the instigation of his father, Apollo, who thought his son could help solve a difficult problem being encountered, not only by the islanders of Ceos, but, in fact, by all of the islands of the Cyclades roundabout them: the Dog-star Sirius was scorching everything, and the crops were failing.

"What Aristaeus did, clever fellow, was to build a gigantic altar to Zeus the Rain-god, and also offered ritual sacrifices on the mountains to Sirius and indeed to Zeus, the son of Cronos, himself. This did the trick. Zeus sent annual winds—the Etesian Winds—each summer, for forty days, to cool the land down, and I've heard that even today the priests on Ceos offer sacrifices before the rising of Sirius, the Dog-star, trying to ensure that the Etesian Winds return for their annual visit. Now there are…"

"That will do, young Peleus," interrupted Phineus, "and congratulations on remembering your lessons in Mythology so well. It's a pity Jason here has apparently forgotten some of his Mythology, though I dare say he has other knowledge which will serve him well on this expedition."

"But…" I said.

"So you will all," Phineus continued, ignoring me, "have to sit around here for forty days until the Etesian Winds have blown themselves out, and you get a chance of some good southerlies. However, you will be very welcome here, and you will all be advised to keep yourselves fit by games and exercises, so that the *Argo* gets full fifty-oar power at maximum strength for her journey up the straits and, I hope, through the Symplegades.

"Oh, I can hear the villagers coming with supplies."

And in through the doorway came twenty-nine of Phineus's friends and neighbours from the nearby villages, bringing barrow-loads of fresh produce from their farms and small-holdings.

One of them, whose name was Paraebius, spoke:

"Greetings to all you noble Argonauts. Old What's-his-name? here, who visited you yesterday, told us who you were, and when, shortly after leaving you, he saw the two sons of Boreas chasing after those dreadful birds yesterday, he assumed that the Harpies problem had been dealt with at last.

"So we have brought you all some food, and, with your permission, will continue to do so for the next forty days, now that the Etesians have started, and sailing northwards is out of the question. Or are we assuming too much?"

"Spot on!" said Phineus. "And you are more than kind to offer to feed us all for the next forty days. But why don't you sit down and have a good chat with these noble Argonauts, now that you are here? And why don't you join us for lunch? By the look of it, there is enough food and drink for all eighty of us."

In fact there were eighty-two of us, but perhaps Phineus had forgotten to include Zetes and Calais. More likely though, he may have miscounted the new arrivals; after all he did suffer from partial blindness!

After lunch, the villagers each enjoyed brief prophetic consultations with Phineus and returned home. Paraebius was the last to leave, and Phineus asked him to return with two sheep from his flock, so that we could offer sacrifices that evening to Apollo, the lord of prophesy (and also have another good feast!).

"Good lad, that!" said Phineus, after Paraebius had left to fetch the sheep. "He used to be in a terrible state. The harder he worked, the poorer he became until he was at his wit's end. And all because of an act of stupidity by his father! What had happened was that his father recklessly cut down the stump of an oak tree in which lived an Hamadryad, who asked him fervently not to do so. But he ignored her prayers, and cut it down in spite of them. Well, that was asking for trouble, wasn't it? The nymph made her death a curse, to him and to his children. So Paraebius never had a chance in life, until he came to me one day, and I advised him to build an altar to the nymph and offer an atoning sacrifice on it. That did the trick, and Paraebius has been almost embarrassingly thankful to me ever since."

"I think it's wonderful, what you do to help the locals," I said. "But you'll have to be careful not to carry your generosity too far in future. You don't want to upset Zeus again, do you?"

"Yes," he replied. "I think I've learnt my lesson. But I

enjoy acting as a kind of social worker and careers advisor, as well as giving a little weather-forecasting and limited travel advice, like I gave you last night. If I restrict myself to that kind of thing, I guess I'll keep my slate clean as far as Zeus is concerned."

And so, for forty days, we enjoyed Phineus's hospitality, and passed the time in games and exercise and a little foraging (to keep in practice). We also partly rebuilt Phineus's palace, with a wooden roof over the main room, and rebuilt his shelter so that the room became a comfortable bed-sitter with enough table-space for him to entertain his friends and neighbours from the village.

Then, dead on time, on the forty-first day, the winds changed and we got a good southerly, and Tiphys said, "It's time to be off!"

40

The Clashing Rocks

We had loaded *Argo* with as many provisions as we dared, and replenished our fresh-water supplies from the pure springs which supplied Phineus and his neighbours.

One of the villagers presented us with a dove in a little wicker cage, which I told Euphemus to look after.

We said our fond farewells to Phineus and his neighbours who came to cheer us on our way, raised an altar to the blessed twelve and left offerings thereon, checked that our furled sail was secure to the gangway, and cast off. We manned all fifty oars right from the start, knowing that the maximum power would be needed in the near future.

The further we travelled, the louder sounded the crash of water against cliffs and of rock against rock. As we rounded the next corner, Tiphys and I saw them—the Symplegades.

My legs melted under me, such was the terror with which those Clashing Rocks affected me. I had been frightened before, but never like this. Tiphys shouted to the crew to take a quick look so that they could see what they were up against.

"Keep rowing," he shouted, "or the current will spin us."

I thought frantically of what Phineus had told me to do. I remembered.

"Euphemus!" I shouted. "Let the dove go and send her forward into those rocks!"

He responded immediately, and the dove flew, as though by instinct, into the space between the rocks, just as they were crashing together.

CRASH!

"The poor bird," I thought, "must have been crushed, must have been."

Then I looked up over the rocks and saw her flying away high above them, but with a flurry of her tail-feathers fluttering behind her in the wind.

"Right," I said to Tiphys. "Let's go for it!"

"Full power!" yelled Tiphys to the crew. "Give it all you've got!"

And they did. We surged forward, and it felt like someone

had kicked *Argo* up the stern. As the rocks drew apart, we rowed into that dreadful chasm.

But as we did so, I saw a mountainous wave bearing down on us.

In a flash I realised what had caused it. When the rocks had closed together, the waters of the Black Sea had piled up against them, frustrated in their desire to rush down the Bosporus. But then the rocks drew apart, and, of course, the pent-up force of the Sea released a mountainous wave to hurl itself down the chasm. And we were in its path!

I shouted to Tiphys, "Look out!"

"I'm not blind," he replied. "Hold this steering oar like you did last time!"

I did as he said. He grasped the other one, and snapped out precise commands to the crew.

I still don't remember how he did it, but we climbed up that wave and slid down the other side even more smoothly than on the previous occasion.

"Pull for your lives," shouted Tiphys to the crew.

"But we've done it!" I said to him.

"No we haven't," said Tiphys, "and we're making no headway at all! The current is too strong for us! In fact we're being carried backwards! Just look at those rocks! They should seem to be moving backwards, not forwards! And now they're starting to move towards us! Start praying!"

I did, so did Tiphys, and so did the rest of the crew. We thought we were done for.

And then…something wonderful happened. We all heard Athena speak from her image at *Argo*'s prow, the image carved into the oak beam from the sacred oak of Dodona, the image which Athena herself had fitted there.

We all heard Athena cry, "Let's go, *Argo!*" and we shot forward like an arrow.

We didn't quite make it. As the rocks crashed together, they caught *Argo*'s stern and crushed the rear of the keel where it curved upwards and forwards over the back of the quarterdeck where Tiphys and I were standing—just as they had caught the tail-feathers of our dove.

But we were still sea-worthy, and Tiphys steered us out of the straits and then a short distance westwards to a sheltered beach a few miles along the European coast of the Black Sea, away from the currents which converge on the Bosporus straits. There we beached and rested, trying to recover our senses.

41

Rest and Reflection

It was early afternoon as we lay on the beach, watching the waves lap against *Argo*'s stern.

Argus told us how he had actually seen Athena give us the required force to beat the Clashing Rocks.

"Jason," he said, "I must tell you this: just as I prayed for *Argo*'s safety back there, I somehow knew that Athena would not let her beloved ship be smashed to smithereens. And, immediately, as I was staring past Tiphys at the helm, there behind him I saw the apparition of Athena herself, holding back the rock on our port side with her left hand

and propelling *Argo* forward with her right. She smiled at me as she did so. Then, as we cleared the rocks, apart from the stern section, Athena seemed to float away upwards in the spray, back towards Olympus."

Argus and I climbed back on board to inspect the damage. He asked my permission for a party to help him look for some suitable timber to replace the smashed section. Personally I thought that the curved ornamental piece was not strictly necessary, and I had knocked my head on it frequently as I walked about the quarterdeck. But Argus was insistent. All galleys ended like that at the rear, he said, and he didn't want *Argo* to become the laughing-stock of the maritime world. Of course, I let him have his way. He soon found a good tree and he spent the rest of the day with his adze, carving and fitting the missing decoration.

I was feeling elated and dejected, all at the same time. Elated, because we had got safely through the Symplegades, and, according to Phineus, could now continue with our voyage, sailing along the south coast of the Black Sea to our destination at Colchis. Dejected, because it suddenly struck me that I had subjected fifty-four of the most noble men of Greece to some extreme perils, and had already lost, or rather abandoned, three of them on the way.

Before we started to prepare for our evening customary sacrifice to a deity and evening meal, I decided to make a short speech to my comrades:

"My friends, tonight we must offer sacrifices and thanksgivings to Athena for saving us all from certain death back there in those dreadful rocks. But I believe that we have saved mankind from their threat forever. Phineus told me privately that if ever a ship passed safely through their jaws, they would never clash again, but be permanently fixed to the sea-bed, affording to future sailors a passage which would be secure from their instability if not from the treacherous currents still flowing through them.

"However, I wish to bare my feelings and confess to you that I wish that we had never started on this dangerous venture, or, at least, that I did not feel myself so responsible for leading all of you into a such continuous stream of perils. We have met quite a few of them on our journey so far, but there are, I feel sure, many more still to be met by us. I think you will agree that we have now passed the point of no return, and we must go on. But if you wish to appoint another leader and captain for the rest of the venture, please do so, because the burden of holding your fates in these hands of mine is one which I find almost too heavy to carry."

I studied their faces while I waited for their reaction. I expected to see signs of protest, but they seemed bored rather than agitated. Telamon eventually stood up, yawned, and spoke:

"I haven't spoken much on this trip so far, but I think I speak for my brother Peleus and myself, and indeed for everyone present, when I say, dear Jason, that we all love you dearly, we support you fully on this great adventure, we're all enjoying it despite the dangers, and have the greatest confidence in your leadership. Nobody else here feels capable of carrying your heavy burden with such flair, and we are sure you will make our expedition a success with the minimum of casualties among us in doing so. We all look forward to retrieving the Golden Fleece for Greece, to enjoying the prosperity which its return to our homeland will secure and the glory which will accrue to us and to our families and to our descendants.

"So please stop blethering on about your sense of insecurity and get with it!"

He sat down to a tumultuous cheer from the assembled company and I felt relieved by what he had said. I think he was a little unfair to suggest, I think, that my speeches were perhaps somewhat verbose, but it was good to know that I had their support.

"Thank you, noble Telamon," I responded, "and all of you for your support. I'll do my best to carry on as your leader and captain.

"Now that we have rested, we must prepare for our feast. Tomorrow, weather permitting, we shall cross the entrance to the straits and sail eastward along the coast."

After our feast in honour of Athena, Peleus sat down with me for a chat.

"Well done, Jason, old pal," he said. "That was a close shave back there with those rocks, but I felt sure we would get through somehow. And didn't old Telamon speak well— never thought he had it in him, but there you are.

"Incidentally, why don't we have a rota of the deities to whom we sacrifice each time we have a feast? Zeus, Hera, Athena, Phoebus Apollo, Poseidon and Aphrodite, and on the seventh occasion to the 'Blessed Twelve'—in case any one of the other six get offended."

"Who are the other six?" I asked him, thinking to catch him out.

Peleus thought and answered, "Demeter, Hermes, Hephaestus, Artemis, Hestia and Ares. Why? Your memory of our Mythology lessons seems to be failing you these days, old boy. Still, as you said, you've had a lot of stress recently. Anyway, what do you think of my suggestion?"

"Sounds a good idea to me," I replied. "I'll discuss it with Idmon and Mopsus, our two resident prophets, and put it into action, if they agree."

Peleus hesitated, and then asked me quietly if I had something for his blisters. "But don't tell the others where they are," he said. I looked.

"How many are there?" he asked.

"Seven," I said.

42

The Isle of Thynias

Early next morning we set sail, taking advantage of a slight westerly breeze. I decided, after consulting with Tiphys, that we would alter the rowing schedule with three teams of the oarsmen on duty at any one time, while the other two rested. We thought that, for normal conditions, this would be sustainable for longer periods, and would enable us to take advantage of light breezes or calms for longer periods of travel, perhaps through several days or nights at a time. Tiphys said that night travel was no problem in favourable weather and when the stars made navigation easy and moonlight kept the coastline visible. Of course, landing for overnight eating and sleeping was preferable when these conditions did not apply, but then there was always the danger that we might not get a friendly reception from the natives.

And so we followed the coastline eastward, passing the locations which Phineus had described: the River Rhebas, the peak of Colone, the Black Cape and then the mouth of the River Phyllis. It was here that Phrixus, during his flight on the golden ram from Orchomenus to Colchis, had been entertained by Dipsacus, who was the son of a meadow-nymph and the River Phyllis; he was a gentle soul who lived with his mother by his father's stream and was quite content to spend his whole life grazing his flocks of sheep by the seaside. As we rowed past his shrine by the riverbank, I wondered, remembering my pleasant days farming on the flanks of Mount Pelion, whether Dipsacus had been cleverer than me. However…

By early dawn the next day, we were approaching the deserted island of Thynias and the calm through which we had been rowing seemed to be ending. The weather was turning sultry with worrying eddies and swirling gusts of wind, threatening a storm, so I thought.

"I don't like the look of the weather," said Tiphys. "We'd better go ashore for a while, until we see how it develops."

As soon as we had beached, Idmon, the prophet, came up to me, and asked permission to address the assembled crew.

"Of course you may," I agreed.

"As you know," he said, turning to the Argonauts as they lay resting on the beach, "although my mortal father is Abas, the son of Melampus, the son of Jason's Uncle Amythaon, my real father is actually Apollo. The reason for this rather uncanny feeling in the air is that my father is travelling on a special journey from Lycia to visit the numerous far-distant peoples of the North. As his son and prophet, I have been told that this island is directly under his path and, with any luck, we should see him fly over very soon."

Every eye turned towards the south, and you could almost have heard one blink. The sighting of a god, even in those heroic days, was a rare occurrence, and I half-expected that Apollo would fly past us without our even glimpsing him. Far from it! We all quite clearly saw him come speeding over the distant hills, then over the sea between us and the mainland, and then right over our heads. We could even see his features! His golden locks flowed in clusters beside his cheeks, in his left hand was a silver bow and on his back was slung a quiver. As he passed, the whole island quaked beneath our feet and the surf surged high on the shore.

He disappeared as quickly as he had come, but the whole ship's crew seemed to have been turned to stone, such was the terror instilled in them by Apollo's passing.

Orpheus broke the silence:

"Today we have been privileged to see the great god Apollo. Let us pray that his appearance be propitious for us. We must build him an altar here on the seashore and offer him suitable sacrifices. It is possible that we could find a fawn and maybe a wild goat in that forest over there. And we shall promise that, if he let us return safe and sound to our homes in Thessaly, we will lay on his altar the thighs of horned goats. In the meantime, let us appease him with sacrifice and libation."

Then turning his head to the clouds in the North, and raising his arms aloft, he prayed:

"Be gracious, O Lord, be gracious in your appearance to us!"

I did not hesitate to send a party into the forest to seek the animals and I organised the building of an altar made of shingle from the beach. And Apollo, I am sure, helped us find a fawn and a goat which, with pious rites, we sacrificed, wrapping their thigh bones in fat and burning them on the altar, celebrating Apollo, Lord of the Dawn.

And we danced in a ring round the altar, and Orpheus, accompanying himself on his lyre, sang a song, celebrating Apollos's exploits.

The crew were in a highly emotional state. They all seemed keen, after they had honoured Apollo, to swear an oath, with holy libations and touching the sacrifice as they swore, that they would, for ever and ever, help each other in the bonds of their friendship.

I suppose this should have cheered me mightily. After all, one of the things which worried me about leading this expedition was the danger of fifty-odd nobles squabbling with each other. Swearing oaths of eternal friendship was all very well, but I remembered Cheiron and his wife Chariclo, and, indeed, my own father and mother—both couples divinely devoted to each other but prone nevertheless to indulge in tempestuous though trivial tiffs from time to time.

"You're a sceptic," said Peleus to me, when the oaths were finished.

"How do you know what I was thinking?" I responded.

"Only got to look at the expression on your face," he said. "Anyway, time for bed!"

43

Lycus and the Mariandyni

The weather next day was blustery and the sea choppy. So we spent the day foraging for supplies and making minor necessary repairs to the *Argo*'s structure and sail.

Early the following morning, a fair westerly breeze favoured our setting sail and we cruised at a cracking pace eastward along the coast. After a few hours we passed the mouth of the great River Sangarius (the modern Sakarya Nehri). Then, about thirty miles further on, the coast line curved gradually northwards until it reached the Acherousian headland (modern Baba Burun) whose steep cliffs jutted out westward, surrounded by smooth rocks over which the waves rolled and thundered. It formed a natural sheltered bay to its south into which flowed the River Lycus, named after king Lycus of the Mariandyni, one of whom, you may remember, we had met after Polydeuces had killed Amycus and we had routed the Bebrycians.

As we passed the Anthemoeisian Marsh (the name derived from a daughter of king Lycus) I recalled what Phineus had told us about this mysterious region.

Inland from the headland a hollow glen sloped away, in the side of which, overarched by rocks and bracken, was the cave of Hades. From its depths issued a chill wind which formed a glistening white frost on the surrounding foliage. Even more frightening was the outfall of the River Acheron which, forcing its way through a deep ravine, bursts forth through the Acherousian headland itself and cascades into the Black Sea.

In spite of which, we decided to land in the shelter of the bay, where we found a natural harbour close by the city of King Lycus (which I believe was on the later site of Heraclea Pontica, modern Eregli).

We had scarcely beached *Argo* when hundreds of the Mariandyni came flocking down to greet us. Leading them was King Lycus himself, full of smiles.

"Welcome to our land, noble Argonauts!" he cried. "We knew you'd make it past the Symplegades and visit us on your brave journey. Which one of you is Polydeuces?"

"My name is Jason," I replied rather stiffly, "and I am the leader of the expedition and captain of our great galley, the *Argo*. Polydeuces, if you wish to speak to him, is over there."

"Oh my dear Jason," Lycus responded. "How very, very rude of me. Please forgive my bad manners. My name is Lycus, and I am king of the Mariandyni here. It's just that I was so eager to meet the hero who actually killed that brute Amycus. We've been hoping someone would do that for many years now. The Bebryces have been a constant menace, ever since Heracles left us, and now you have so thrashed them that I believe they may very well leave us alone for a while."

"You say that Heracles left you? When was that?" I asked, hoping that it was recently and that we could catch up with him again.

"Oh, many years ago now," he replied. "But I will tell you all about it later, and you must tell me all about your expedition. All of you, come with us back to my palace, where I hope you will spend at least one night with us, and this evening we shall have a banquet, indeed we shall!"

"Thank you, kind sir!" I replied. "But please do meet Polydeuces now, since you have been itching to speak to him."

Polydeuces came over and Lycus and his companions flocked round him. Such was their enthusiasm to talk to the killer of their great enemy, Amycus, that I feared for his safety, though I am sure he could have boxed his way out of the scrum. All was well, however, and we eventually made our way up the slope to Lycus's palace.

We were looked after like royalty. We bathed and drank wine and rested until evening came, when we were ushered into the main hall. There a magnificent spread had been prepared for us, and we took our places on the couches with all the senior leaders of the Mariandyni.

I was positioned on Lycus's right and (as I expected) Polydeuces was on his left. We had a good gossip.

"Yes," said Lycus, "Heracles was here many years ago, when my father, Dascylus, was king. He was passing through here on his way back from the land of the Amazons, where, as one of his labours, he had acquired Hippolyte's girdle. I expect he told you all about it?"

"Yes," I said. "Quite often, though he didn't mention passing through here."

"Very shy, that Heracles," continued Lycus. "Well, while he was here, he boxed with the mighty Titias at the funeral games for my brother Priolas, and knocked out all his teeth!"

"Who was Titias?" I asked.

"That's rather a long story," he replied, which I'll tell you some other time. Anyway, Heracles brought the Mysians (who had killed my brother Priolas), as well as the Mygdones (who dwelt on our borders), under my father's sovereignty. Not only that, but he conquered the land and tribes of the people of Bithynia right as far as the River Rhebas and peak of Colone."

"We passed by them on our journey here," I commented.

"Well, you would do, coming along the coast," Lycus continued. "Then Heracles conquered the Paphlagonians to our east, who live round the River Billaios. You'll see that too as you travel on along the coast."

"I hope so," I said.

"However," he continued, "since Heracles left us all those years ago, Amycus and the Bebrycians have been plundering our land right up to the River Hypios and its marshes."

"But now," he said, turning to Polydeuces, "thanks to our noble friend here, we hope that they have been taught a lesson and will not trouble us again for some time. That day when you killed Amycus, and you all routed them into the hills, we had been trying to do the same, but not with much success."

"We met one of your guards," I said, "and he told us all about it before following after you. I forgot to ask his name."

"Ah," said Lycus, "that would have been old…um…what's-his-name? He told me what it was the other day, but I forget now. Begins with a letter 'T' or perhaps it was a 'P'. Anyway, I hope he explained things to you and gave you any help and told you we left some provisions for you."

"Indeed he did," I said. "I would like to meet him again before we leave."

"Of course," said Lycus. "In fact, it will be difficult to avoid him. He's on palace-door duty most of the time. But you must tell me all about your companions and your journey here."

So I spent the next hour or so telling him the names and brief biographical details of each of my fifty-one companions. Then I described how we had been entertained by the ladies of Lemnos and by Cyzicus and the Doliones; how we had lost Heracles and Hylas and Polyphemus and how Glaucus told us to carry on without them; how Polydeuces had killed Amycus and how we had routed the Bebryces; how we had saved Phineus from the Harpies and of his prophesies; how Athena had helped us through the Clashing Rocks and how we all saw Apollo himself on his journey north over the isle of Thynias.

By the time I had finished I noticed that Lycus had nodded off. In fact everyone else had gone to bed. I gently shook Lycus, who must have been very tired after all the excitement of the day, and he said:

"Very interesting. Time for bed, I think. I have something very important to tell you, but it's a bit late now. I'll tell you tomorrow morning, before you leave. You will remind me, won't you?"

I said I would, and we too went to bed.

44

A Time for Grief

I was up before the others next morning and decided to take a stroll round the palace to stretch my legs. As I passed through the front doors:

"Hi there!" came a voice. "Remember me?"

"Of course I do," I replied. "You're old 'What's-his-name?' as Lycus calls you."

"He never could remember my name," the guard laughed. "Anyway, I'm glad to see you got here safely. It must have been a bit dodgy getting through those clashing rocks back there."

"You can say that again," I responded.

"I said it must have been a bit...but here comes King Lycus," he said.

"Good morning, all," said Lycus. "May I join you, young Jason, if you're stretching your legs round the palace?"

"Of course," I said. "By the way, you asked me last night to remind you that you had something important to tell me this morning."

"Did I really?" he said. "Oh yes, so I did. Two things actually. Firstly, I intend to build a lofty temple on the Acherusian height, to be a landmark for all future sailors to see and be guided by—so they know where they are, you know."

"May I ask whether this temple is in honour of anyone

in particular?" I asked, thinking how pleasant it would be to have a temple built in my honour.

"In honour of the sons of Tyndareus, Castor and Polydeuces, of course. I'm surprised you asked. But it's time to go in for breakfast. This morning air gives one an appetite, you know."

"What was the second important thing you had to tell me?" I asked rather coldly.

"Second thing?…Oh, yes. With your permission, I'm sending my son Dascylus on board with you (same name as my father, you know), to help you as a guide as far as the mouth of the River Thermodon, which is well over half way of the distance between here and Colchis. He knows all the tribes along that stretch, and can advise you where to land for your sleepovers, as well as warning you of some of the adverse, if not dangerous, currents along that bit of coast."

"That's very kind of you," I said, as we started breakfast. "We shall need all the help we can get."

Then, after breakfast, Lycus insisted on accompanying us from the palace down to the harbour. His guards and companions came as well in great numbers, carrying an embarrassing quantity of gifts for us.

Lycus, his son Dascylus and I were chatting amiably at the rear of this great procession when tragedy struck.

We were walking along the bank of the river which led from the city to the harbour. The ground all around was marshy. Concealed among the high reeds lurked a huge white-tusked boar, a monstrous and deadly beast. Lycus told me later that nobody had been able to find its lair and that it had from time immemorial ranged unchecked throughout the marshes, terrifying even the nymphs of the water-meadows.

Somehow we must have disturbed it for it came thundering out of the reed-beds and plunged into the procession ahead of us. We heard a shriek of agony from one of our number. Next I saw Peleus hurling his spear at the beast as it withdrew into the reed-beds. But it turned again and charged, and we could see it still carrying Peleus's spear in its side. Then I saw Idas aiming his spear at it. This time the beast caught it deep in its flank and died with a terrible roar. Idas, who (you may remember) boasted irreverently on the beach at Pagasae that his spear would protect us more surely than could even Zeus himself, had proved his worth. There was no boasting this time. He shouted back to me: "Idmon's been hurt—come quickly, Jason!"

I ran forward to where Idmon had fallen. The boar had gashed his thigh, severing the sinews and the bone. I recalled all that Cheiron had taught me, staunching the blood flow as best I could, but the injury was too severe. Idmon died in my arms.

Thus Idmon fulfilled his prophesy that he would die on the journey.

Of course all thought of sailing was abandoned. We returned to the city and for three whole days we lamented our senior prophet's death. Then we buried him, and King Lycus and his people joined in the funeral rites. We raised his barrow a little below the Acherusian headland, and near it, as a memorial for him, we shaped a wild olive tree to resemble one of the large rollers we had used to launch the *Argo* at Pagasae.

As we returned to the city from the funeral, Peleus drew level with me.

"I don't want to worry you at a time like this," he said, "but I'm worried about Tiphys. He was too ill to come to the funeral, and he really has a terrible fever."

I must confess I hadn't missed him at the funeral. I had been too upset to count the Argonauts, as was my practice from time to time and at least once each day. I cursed myself for my incompetence.

"Why didn't somebody tell me?" I asked.

"Well," replied Peleus, "you did seem rather preoccupied with grief at the time."

We hurried back to the city and into the room at the palace where Tiphys was asleep but restless. Lycus came in and said:

"Looks like marsh fever. He's still young and fit. He'll get over it."

I administered some of Cheiron's medicine which I remembered he had often used to alleviate a fever.

But not this particular type of fever. The locals had obviously become immune to it over many generations. But Tiphys had no immunity to it.

He died during the night.

We lamented him for three more days and buried him next to Idmon.

45

We journey on

Several days after the burial of Tiphys (I'm afraid I had rather lost track of the days) I was sitting on the beach in the shade of *Argo*'s prow, feeling utterly despondent and wondering how to tell the crew I had almost decided to call off the expedition.

I had my head in my hands and felt somebody sit down by my side. It was Peleus. We said nothing for quite a long time. Eventually, and with difficulty, I broke the silence:

"Thank you, Peleus. What's the matter?"

"Well," he replied, "the crew have held a meeting while you've been down here. They have agreed that we should put aside our grief and continue with our enterprise."

"And how many more of them," I asked, "must die before we return home with the wretched fleece, always assuming that we can recover it?"

"I've no idea," he replied. "Perhaps Mopsus can find out; I'll ask him sometime. Anyway, we felt we needed a new helmsman. There were four volunteers: Nauplius, Euphemus, Erginus and Ancaeus. Ancaeus won the vote by a large majority, subject, of course, to your approval."

"You do mean Ancaeus, the son of Poseidon and brother of Erginus," I asked, "and not Ancaeus, the son of Lycurgus, who used to row opposite Heracles, don't you?"

"Yes, of course," Peleus replied with a chuckle. "Anyway,

let's get back to the palace, because Lycus has laid on a farewell banquet for us. He'll be so upset if we miss it."

Back to the palace we walked, and spent our last night there in the pleasant company of Lycus and the Mariandyni.

Early next morning we repeated our procession with Lycus and his people along the riverbank down to the harbour and the *Argo*, this time without incident.

And so, on the twelfth day (so Peleus said), we said our farewells, went aboard and set sail with a strong breeze of westerly wind filling *Argo*'s sail. It felt good to be at sea again; I was beginning to get a taste for it.

I had to re-arrange the rowing rosters: I decided that Zetes and Calais should return to their permanent flying duties. Orpheus returned to time-setting and making morale-boosting music. Lycus's son Dascylus (he had no experience of rowing) would act as guide and adviser and stay with Orpheus, Ancaeus and me on the quarterdeck. This left forty-five crew available for rowing-teams, so I decided to ask Argus to be in full-time charge of running repairs and rigging (he seemed quite pleased). So I reduced three of the five teams from ten to eight rowers. I also decided that under normal, favourable conditions, only three teams would be rowing at any one time, which meant that each team could relax for two out of every five periods of rowing duty. This gave a minimum of twenty-four, and maximum of twenty-eight rowers at any one time. Of course, when conditions demanded, I could order four or even five teams to be on active duty, which gave Ancaeus, our new helmsman, a considerable degree of flexibility in available motive power.

Peleus said he couldn't understand my new roster system,

but he expected to get the hang of it when the need arose. In the meantime, while we were under sail, he'd try to humour his hangover (Lycus had indulged us with some of his best wine the previous evening).

Ancaeus proved to be a very competent helmsman; his experience was considerable and he was popular with the crew. I instructed him to take us at an easy pace along the coast towards our destination, beaching for the night whenever possible unless a prevailing westerly and a starlit sky could ensure safe and leisurely sailing through the hours of darkness.

Keeping Phineus's prophesies in mind, our next objective was the Isle of Ares, and it took us twenty-one days before we sighted it. In the meantime, Dascylus guided us skilfully and his knowledge of the coastline, its bays, mountains, rivers and peoples was of inestimable value.

During the next twenty days, we passed by:

The outfall of the River Callichorus, where they say Dionysus once held his rites and established dances in front of the cave.

Then the tomb of Sthenelus, son of Actor. On his way back with Heracles from war against the Amazons he was struck by an arrow and died there on the beach. As we were passing, we actually saw him standing on his barrow. We presumed he had prevailed upon Persephone for leave to watch us pass by—warriors like he himself had once been. We felt highly honoured, and Mopsus urged us to land and appease him with libations and sacrifices of sheep. We also built an altar to Apollo there, and burnt thigh-bones for him and Orpheus dedicated his lyre to him.

Next the stream of Parthenius, a gentle river, where it

was said Artemis cools her limbs after the heat of the chase. Then Sesamus and lofty Erythini, Crobialus, Cromna and woody Cytorus, Cape Carambis and the long strand of Aegialus.

Eventually Cape Sinope, so named after Sinope, daughter of Asopus, who succeeded in keeping her virginity, tricking not only Apollo but Zeus himself into getting them to promise her whatever her heart desired, which turned out to be her virginity. Clever girl!

Then the village of Sinope itself (round the corner beyond the tricky cape) where we gained three new crew members: Deileon, Autolycus and Phlogius. They were the sons of Deimachus of Tricca who had accompanied Heracles on his expedition against the Argonauts. Somehow they got separated from the main party on its return, and they decided to settle in Sinope. Dascylus had heard rumours that they were still there, were getting fed up with it and wanted to leave it for good. We nearly didn't call there, because we were enjoying the luxury of a brisk north-west wind, but I decided the three of them might be willing to supplement our depleted crew, and so it proved. When they were on board, Peleus said that they upset my roster-plan, but I asked the three of them to elect two of their number to join one of the teams of eight. Argus said he would join with the third brother to join yet another team of eight if circumstances demanded it. Peleus said it was all getting too complicated, but Ancaeus said he couldn't care less, as long as he had enough oar power at his disposal and he left the details to me.

The rivers Halys (modern Kizilirmak) and Iris (modern Yesilirmak) followed, and the delta-land of Assyria, and then we rounded the headland of Amazon country. In the bay of this headland, there is the outfall of the River Thermodon (modern Terme Çay) with its ninety-six channels fanning out to reach the sea. We had to land there briefly, firstly because the sea was becoming too choppy for comfort and secondly to put Dascylus ashore. I was worried for him, in view of the proximity of the three tribes of Amazons, but he said he knew a safe way home; he said he would buy horse from a friendly village and be home in next to no time. I asked him to quantify this, but he simply smiled and thanked me for the trip. It was hereabouts that Heracles caught Melanippe, the daughter of Ares, and acquired her sister Hippolyte's girdle as Melanippe's ransom. These Amazons were the daughters of Ares, the god of war, and of the nymph Harmonia. All they cared about was grievous insolence and the works of Ares. We did not hang about there, despite the choppy sea.

The land of the Chalybes came next. Dascylus had told me that they did no farming: no ploughing, no vines nor fruit trees, no flocks of sheep nor herds of cattle. They dug for iron ore, smelted it and sold it in exchange for their food and other requirements.

Next we rounded the headland of Genetaian Zeus near the River Genes and sailed past the country of the Tibareni. According to Dascylus, the men used to go into phantom labour when their wives were in childbirth. It was the husbands who took to their beds, and lay there groaning with their heads wrapped in wet cloths, while their wives fed them and bathed them. Peleus wanted to stop and see if it was true, but I put my foot down.

Then we passed the Sacred Mountain and the highlands

where the Mossynoeci live in their *mossynes* or wooden houses. They too had strange customs, which were almost the opposite of ours. Things which we used to do openly, such as trading, they carried out privately indoors, whereas what we were accustomed to do privately indoors, such as making love, they performed openly out-of-doors. Also, if their king dispensed judgement and they thought it was wrong, they locked him up without food for the rest of the day. Again I had to put my foot down with Peleus.

Then came the twenty-first day after leaving Lycus and the Mariandyni. We had been cruising along comfortably but suddenly the gentle breeze left us. So we restarted rowing, when, as it seemed from nowhere, a dagger-like feather pierced Oileus on his left shoulder; he dropped his oar and collapsed in agony.

46

The Island of Ares

Eribotes was sitting right behind Oileus; he immediately drew out the feather and bound up the wound with his scabbard strap. Before I could reach him with my own first-aid kit, another bird swooped down to the attack. But Clytius, son of Eurytus, swiftly sped an arrow at it and struck it; it whirled round and fell dead into the sea.

Zetes and Calais circled round and reported that the arrow which had killed the bird had frightened off any other bird which had been in the area, and that there was no immediate danger from another attack. I attended to Oileus with a suitable ointment; he smiled and said he thought he would survive.

Amphidamas, son of Aleus, came up to me and asked if he could address the crew. I agreed.

"We are obviously getting near the island of Ares. Those birds are certainly the birds which defend it. The question is: how can we land without further injuries from their dagger-like feathers? Well, I think I have the answer. I was actually there when Heracles came to Arcadia. He had trouble with the birds there, which swam on the Stymphalian lake. He tried arrows from his bow—useless! But then he shook in his hand a rattle made of bronze, and the loud clatter it made frightened off those birds, and away they flew, screeching in an almighty panic. You should have heard them! So, based on that experience, I have a cunning plan, and here it is: Everyone who has one, which I think is most of you, puts on his crested helmet. Then we row using, say, only two teams, and the rest of us fence the ship about with our spears and shields, and, as we approach the island, we scare the birds with shouting and nodding our crests and waving our spears. Then, when we reach the island, we create a din by clashing our shields. What do you think?"

We approved his plan in principle, though, after consulting with Ancaeus, Orpheus and Argus, I decided that the best form of defence would be to create a kind of roof over the *Argo*, formed by all the available shields. We rowed steadily forward like this, making as much din as possible. Soon the island came into view, but there was no sign of more birds. In fact we were beginning to feel slightly foolish by the time we beached on the shore of a suitable bay, but suddenly a huge swarm of the birds of Ares rose up from the ground, disturbed by our arrival. Amphidamas's cunning plan actually worked. We clashed our shields with renewed vigour and the birds left the island for the opposite mainland, aiming a dense shower of their beastly dagger-feathers upon our roof of shields as they did so.

I tried to remember what Phineus had told us about this island. He said it was rather inhospitable—true. He said there was a stone altar there which had been built by two queens of the Amazons—there it was. But what was the point of our landing there?—he had declined to tell us. No doubt we would find out in due course. It was quite a small island, not far to the north from the mainland where dwelt those savages, the Mossynoeci. We rather hoped that they had restricted themselves to dwelling on the mainland.

We had been rowing all day and it was late afternoon, time for us to our prepare for our evening meal. I sent several foraging parties out to collect bedding and to look for fresh fruit and nuts and water and perhaps a sheep or two if the island had any.

They came back with all of these—and a surprise. Four scruffy humans who looked as though they had been dragged backwards through a forest of thorn-bushes. They were covered in scars and they looked very tired and frightened.

Their leader approached me. "Please," he said, "whoever you are, please treat us kindly and help us. We have been stranded here for longer than we care to remember, and need to get off this accursed island. There are some aggressive birds here who keep puncturing us with dagger-like feathers, and we cannot stand much more of it."

"I know," I said, "we've met them, but we've scared them off for a while, as least. Do, please, sit down and rest and have something to eat. Some of my crew here will get you some clean clothes from our ship, and we'll all be having a proper feast later on this evening. But, if you feel up to it, perhaps you could tell us who you are and what disaster overtook you."

"Thank you for your kindness," he said. "My name is Argus."

I saw our Argus open his lips, but I motioned to him not to interrupt.

"And these are my three brothers, Melas, Phrontis and Cytissorus. We are the four sons of Phrixus who flew on the golden ram from Orchomenos in Boeotia to the city of Aea, the capital of Colchis at the eastern end of this sea. But you may already have heard of the story of the Golden Fleece."

"Indeed we have," I said. "But here's a surprise for you: all four of you are my second cousins! Greetings!"

"Then who are you?" asked this new Argos (I shall spell his name like this with an 'o' from now onwards, to save confusing him with Argus, the builder of the *Argo*!).

"I am Jason, son of Aeson, son of Cretheus, son of Aeolus, who is your great-grandfather as well as mine, because, as you have just told me, your father is Phrixus, son of Athamas, son of Aeolus. Athamas and Cretheus were brothers. So your grandfather was my great-uncle, and my grandfather was…"

"Yes," said Argos. "I think I've got it. Well, it's a small world, isn't it?"

"So it appears," I replied. "But tell me, how did you four get to be stranded here?"

"Our father, Phrixus, died not long ago, and on his deathbed he told us to sail from Aea to his home in Orchomenos to claim his wealth there. We set sail in a rotten old Colchian ship and were some distance out from the coast when Zeus stirred up for us a wicked north wind. We'd never seen such a storm. It shredded our sail and split our hull in two. Somehow, in spite of the darkness, we managed to cling to one of the huge beams from the shattered ship until it was washed up on to the shore here. We were often tempted to try to swim to the mainland, but we remembered from our geography lessons that the Mossynoeci dwelt there, and we were not too keen to meet them. So we stayed here, plagued and punctured by those pernicious birds, hoping that someone like you would come along and offer to get us away from here."

"And then we came along," I commented.

"Thank heaven you did. But what are you doing here?" he asked. "Who are you all, and where are you heading?"

"Very briefly," I replied, "we are a body of heroes from Greece, called Argonauts, sailing in a galley named *Argo*, bound for Colchis to recover the Golden Fleece and the ghost of your father to bring them back to Iolcos, so that the anger of those in the underworld may be appeased and Iolcos and indeed Greece may be restored to prosperity.

"I hope that covers it in broad terms. But after we have wined and dined this evening, you will no doubt be pleased to hear from me a full account of the names and ancestry

221

of all our Argonauts, how the expedition was conceived and brought to fruition, as well as details of all our adventures on our journey so far."

Argos stood there with his mouth wide open, obviously amazed at his good fortune in being promised a first-hand account of the expedition from its leader.

Soon afterwards we all went to the temple of Ares to offer sacrifice of sheep. The temple was roofless and the altar, constructed of pebbles, was outside. Inside the temple was a black stone. I learnt later that the Amazons used to pray to it, and instead of sheep or oxen, they used to sacrifice horses, of which they kept great herds.

Then followed a very welcome feast. Before I began to delight Phrixus's four sons with my account of the expedition, I decided to ask them for their help on the expedition.

"Dear friends," I said, "you are, of course, very welcome to travel on with us. If you wish, you may get off at Colchis, or, if you are determined to get to Orchomenus to claim your inheritance, you may return with us to Greece with the Fleece. We should welcome you as oarsmen when required, since we are four short of full complement at present."

And I went on to explain the roster system that I had devised, and how they could bring the two teams of eight up to full strength. They seemed somewhat confused about the system, but Peleus said he would explain it to them sometime.

I continued, "In addition, I would welcome any help you can give us towards our recovery of the Fleece. Your local knowledge would be of very great value. You would, of course, be entitled to call yourselves Argonauts, since our expedition is aimed at atoning for the intended sacrifice of your dear father at Orchomenus."

The effect on the four brothers was alarming. They all turned pale and started twitching.

Argos spoke: "Oh dear. Of course we shall be pleased to take our turns at *Argo*'s oars and also to help you with information concerning the geography of the area and the disposal of Aeetes's forces and resources. But we must warn you: Aeetes terrifies us, even though he is our grandfather because he gave one of his daughters, Chalciope, in marriage to Phrixus. He reckons he is son of Helios, the Sun itself, and his supporters are very numerous in all the lands around him. He guards the Fleece jealously, because he regards it as the charm which ensures his power and prosperity. To guard it he has acquired a deathless and sleepless serpent. It is said that Earth itself brought it into being by the rock of Typhaon on the flanks of the Caucasus Mountains. In our opinion, you will never get possession of the Fleece without the permission of Aeetes, and getting that will be very, very tricky. But if you must try to achieve your goal, we will, of course, do our best to help you."

"Have no fear," I replied. "If it comes to a fight, we have over fifty of the bravest and strongest warriors in the whole world on our side, and some of us are related to the gods themselves, many of whom are also on our side and approve our goals. I have every confidence that we shall succeed, particularly now that we have all four of you to help us. A prophet named Phineus told us to land on this island, and that advice would not have been given us without good reason, I think.

"But I have promised to tell you about our crew and the origins of our expedition and our adventures since leaving Pagasae."

I cannot remember talking for more than ten minutes or so. My companions kept replenishing my wine-goblet. Talking is thirsty work and the wine was of such a good vintage that I drank, perhaps, more than I needed.

I awoke next morning tucked up in very comfortable bedding, but with a terrible headache. The four sons of Phrixus and, indeed, all my companions were busying themselves with preparing for the next stage of our voyage. They all had wide grins on their faces, so I presumed they had all enjoyed the feast the previous evening, and, especially no doubt, my talk. However, I must confess, I couldn't remember much about it.

We sailed soon afterwards, with Ancaeus temporarily in charge.

47

We arrive at Colchis

It was tempting to set an east-north-east course for Colchis straight across the huge bay at the eastern end of the Black Sea. The wind was a south-wester and we were now back to full oar-power with fifty-seven of us on board. However, prudence prevailed and Ancaeus agreed with me that the wind might turn against us, and then we might meet the same kind of fate as had been suffered by the four sons of Phrixus.

So we decided to plod on round the coast, which changed direction gradually from eastwards to northwards. We sailed whenever possible or rowed with only three teams of ten at any one time, to conserve their energies. It took us nine days with stop-overs every night to reach Colchis at the far end of the Black Sea, and we received nothing but friendship whenever we encountered the local tribes.

We passed the Isle of Philyra. This had interest for Peleus and me because this was the island where Cheiron's mother lived when Cronos was surprised by his jealous consort Rhea, changed himself into a horse as a disguise and escaped, but not before Philyra had become pregnant. You may remember the story from when I was describing the staff of Cheiron's School for Heroes.

We passed the lands of the primitive but friendly Macrones, the broad lands of the Becheiri, the supercilious Sapeires and the near-by Byzeres.

And then, at the end of the tenth day we saw our objective: the mouth of the River Phasis, near the banks of which, inland, we had been told was Aea, the city of King Aeetes. Ahead we could see the broad sweep of the Caucasus Mountains, on the crags of which poor Prometheus had been chained, and had suffered every day from the claws and beak of the eagle which had fed on his liver.

We reached the river-mouth as darkness fell. We furled our sail and lowered and stowed our mast. We rowed slowly and carefully, almost silently, forward into the estuary. By the skill of Argus who advised on our draught and Ancaeus our helmsman we crept up the river. On our left we could make out the Caucasus Mountains towering over the city of Aea. On our right was the plain of Ares and his sacred grove, where the dread serpent was guarding the Golden Fleece as it was draped over the leafy branches of an oak.

I took a golden goblet and into the river I poured libations of honey and neat wine, praying to the Earth, to the unknown gods of that country and to the souls of its dead heroes, asking them to welcome us and our ship.

On the advice of Argus, we entered a shady backwater, and moored with our anchor-stones.

Ancaeus addressed the crew: "At last we have reached the River Phasis and the land of Colchis in safety. We shall be quite safe here hidden by the reeds, and we shall sleep on board, at least for tonight, as best we can. In the morning Jason has said that he will tell us what he has decided: whether to speak to Aeetes and try to persuade him to let us have the Golden Fleece, or whether some other course of action will be necessary to achieve our objective."

The crew needed no bidding to curl up and get some sleep. It had been a long and, towards the end, a stressful day.

During the last few days of our journey I had given a great deal of thought to what we would do when we arrived. So I, too, decided to curl up for some sleep under the quarterdeck to ensure maximum freshness for the morning.

What I did not expect was that, during the hours of darkness on board *Argo* that night, I would have the most exciting dream of my lifetime.

48

I have a dream

I was soaring over Mount Olympus, the home of the gods. I felt wool in my hands and between my knees. When I looked down directly under me, I could see the head of a golden ram beneath my chin.

"Hi there, Jason!" said the ram. "Anyone in particular you want to see?"

"I've no idea," I replied. "I didn't ask to be here."

"Even so," said the ram, "it's your dream, not mine. Hey, but I've just spotted Hera and Athena having a chin-wag, in private by the look or it. Care to listen in?"

"Are you sure we'll not be noticed?" I asked.

"No problem," replied the ram. "Dreams are quite insubstantial, you know. Is that near enough for you to hear?"

"What's to be done?" Hera was asking Athena. "I'd like your opinion."

"Yes," I whispered to the ram. "I can hear quite clearly. No closer, please, or we'll be seen."

"Nonsense," said the ram, "but I'll hover here, if you're happy with that."

"What's to be done about what?" asked Athena.

"About Jason, of course," replied Hera. My ears pricked up!

"As we've just seen," she continued, "your good ship *Argo* has eventually arrived at Colchis, and somehow all they have to do now is get the Golden Fleece and sail back

227

to Iolcos. If they don't, then Phrixus's ghost will linger there forever and I shall never see that wretch Pelias get his just deserts. In any case, Jason is a favourite of mine, particularly since the day when he carried me on his shoulders over the swollen river, and he, and indeed all his companions, are in grave danger from Aeetes. Jason will never be able to persuade him to hand over the Fleece, however persuasive he may be. And the Fleece is guarded by that dreadful serpent from the Caucasus, who could gobble up a thousand Argonauts and still not suffer indigestion."

"Well," replied Athena, "I have given the matter a great deal of thought, and have not come up with a single bright idea. Except, perhaps, you could talk Zeus into lending some help with a thunderbolt or two?"

"Out of the question," said Hera. "I've problems enough with him as it is. But how about a little witchcraft? Aeetes has two daughters: Chalciope, the one who married Phrixus, and the younger daughter called Medea. She is a sorceress and the high priestess of that dreadful goddess Hecate. I reckon that, if anyone can help Jason get his hands on the Fleece, then Medea can."

"But how," asked Athena, "can we get Medea to want to help Jason?"

"No problem," replied Hera, "if she falls head-over-heels in love with him. And that's where our friend the goddess Aphrodite can help, if only she can persuade her wayward son Eros to shoot one of his arrows at Medea!"

"What a great idea," enthused Athena. "Why don't we go and pay her a visit without delay? Except that, as far as love-making and all that kind of thing is concerned, I have no experience at all. So perhaps it would be best if you did all the talking when we see her. I don't want to get tongue-tied and look embarrassed."

"Of course, dear," replied Hera. "I quite understand. But let's be off!"

They both shimmered away across the peaks of Olympus.

"Quick!" I said to my ram. "Follow those goddesses!"

"Sure will," replied the ram. "I'm interested too!" and we zoomed away after the goddesses until they arrived at the palace of Aphrodite. They entered its front courtyard and I could see Aphrodite in her front room, sitting on an inlaid chair facing the door and combing her long hair with a golden comb. She looked up and when she saw Hera and Athena, she shouted to them:

"Come in, do! Here's a couple of couches for you! Make yourselves comfortable!"

They did so, and then Aphrodite said, "And to what am I indebted for this visit from you senior goddesses? I can't remember the last time either one of you honoured me with your presence in my humble home."

"Come, come, dear," replied Hera. "Don't be like that. You know how it is, sometimes. But how is your dear husband, Hephaestus?"

"Oh," replied Aphrodite, "he's gone down to his forge and anvils, on that floating island of his, making something or other. But I'm sure you haven't come to ask about him."

"To be quite honest," said Hera, "we're in a bit of a fix, and we think you are the only one who can help us."

Aphrodite smiled with importance.

"You no doubt know," continued Hera, "that Jason and his Argonauts are trying to recover the Golden Fleece from the ram on which…"

"I know, I know," interrupted Aphrodite.

"Well," said Hera, "they have arrived in Colchis, and don't know whether to take the Fleece by force, a course of action which would be extremely dangerous and almost certainly unsuccessful, or to deal with Aeetes, an impossible man to deal with, unless…"

Hera paused. Aphrodite said, "Yes, yes, unless what?"

"…unless," continued Hera, "you can persuade your lovely son, Eros, to shoot one of his arrows at Aeetes's daughter Medea, and make her fall in love with Jason. She is a witch and a priestess of Hecate, and you know what that means! We feel sure that Medea will then do all she can to help Jason achieve his, and indeed our, objectives."

"Brilliant!" said Aphrodite. "Which is what I would expect from the queen of goddesses. Mind you, Eros is very wayward, and it will not be easy. But as you know, I'll do my best for you."

"We are so grateful," said Hera, rising from her couch. "See you later," as she and Athena hastened away.

"I bet I won't," mumbled Aphrodite, as she arose and shot off through the glens of Olympus to find her boy.

"Follow that goddess," I said to my ram.

"No need to shout," he replied. "I'm with you all the way."

Aphrodite found Eros in the orchard of Zeus, playing with Ganymedes, a young boy whom Zeus, attracted by his beauty, had abducted to be his cupbearer. Eros had just beaten Ganymedes at the game of golden dice and Ganymedes went off in a huff.

"I saw you," said Aphrodite. "You were cheating as usual."

"So what?" said Eros. "And if you want anything, the answer is *no*."

"I have here," said Aphrodite, "a golden ball, which Zeus's nurse made for him when he was young. As you can see, its seams are concealed and overlaid with dark-blue spirals, very pretty. But if you toss it up, it leaves behind it a meteor-like trail of golden sparkles. Like this!"

And she tossed it up and caught it again in a cascade of falling lights.

"Want it!" said Eros. "Gimme!"

"No," said his mother. "But I will if you do me a favour."

"Ball first," said Eros, "favour later."

"No," said Aphrodite firmly. "Favour first. Go to Aea, the capital of Colchis, and shoot one of your arrows at Medea, the daughter of King Aeetes. Make her fall in love with Jason. Do this as soon as possible, and if it works, this ball will be yours."

"Oh all right then," said Eros. "But I'll find Ganymedes first, and have another game or two of dice with him."

"Don't leave it too long," said Aphrodite. "Don't leave it too… . Don't leave it…"

I woke up. What a dream! It was still dark. I lay awake pondering the dream. I went over my possible courses of action for the morning. It was obvious what I must do.

49

The Palace of Aeetes

Beneath a leaden sky, dawn spread her silver robes

generously over the river-marshes of the Phasis, and fifty-seven uncomfortable Argonauts stirred in soggy groups of two or three up and down the unforgiving benches of the good ship *Argo*. We washed and breakfasted as best we could, after which I addressed the crew:

"My friends, here is my plan. Before any action on your part, we shall try diplomacy with Aeetes. I know he has a bad reputation, but he did once welcome Phrixus to his land, and he was an asylum-seeker fleeing from his stepmother's jealousy and his father's knife, whereas we come merely with a request to recover something which is legitimately ours. I shall go to his palace with only six of you: the four sons of Phrixus and two others; I have chosen Telamon and Augeias. I cannot believe that, initially at least, we shall come to any harm. It seems unlikely that Aeetes is so shameless that he would transgress the laws of hospitality as required by the ordinances of Zeus, Protector of Guests. I appoint Peleus as my deputy here to be in charge of the other forty-nine of you. You will remain here until we seven return and I can give you news of the latest position and further instructions. If we do not return within twenty-four hours, Peleus will no doubt decide on the best course of action for you. In the meantime, make yourselves as comfortable as possible and guard *Argo* well. I do not think the Colchians have spotted our arrival, but I would not bet on it.

"Does any one of you have any objections to this plan? If so, raise your hand."

Nobody did. I could see Idas hesitating, but he thought better of it.

Seven of us positioned one of Argus's spare planks from

Argo to dry ground across the reed beds. We crossed it and set off northwards up a rising plain towards the city of Aea.

Argos was keen to show the way and describe the features we encountered. It was not far before our path followed the course of a little stream which flowed southwards to join the Phasis. Each side of this grew willow trees from the branches of which hung many hundreds of untanned ox-hides.

"Inside those," commented Argos, "are all the dead male Colchians. This is, in fact, their graveyard. The Colchians do not believe in burying or cremating their dead males. However, they do bury their female dead, believing that earth and air should have equal portions."

I was beginning to wonder whether we would even get to Aeetes's palace in safety, since we would first have to walk through a city inhabited by people who practised such a strange custom, when a dense fog came down. However, Argos and his brothers knew the way even in a fog, and we arrived at the palace gates before I realised that we had been walking through the city.

The fog cleared as suddenly as it had dropped. I observed an old hag by the side of the gates. She looked surprisingly like the one I had helped over the swollen River Anaurus. She winked at me and disappeared. I felt a surge of confidence as we walked in through the gates into the palace courtyard.

We stopped just inside the gates and looked around us. We were impressed. Lofty stone columns surrounded this outer courtyard; grapevines grew in profusion over them, soaring high until they met to form a shady canopy over the whole area.

In the centre were four fountains, gushing from underground springs. Argos told us that Hephaestus had created them for the royal palace; one, he said, flowed with milk, one with wine, the third with fragrant oil and the fourth ran with water, warm in winter and ice-cold in summer.

Argos mentioned that Hephaestus had also made bulls with bronze feet and mouths of bronze from which they breathed frightful flames of fire, as well as a plough fashioned from one piece of solid adamant. I asked him why Hephaestus had been so generous. He explained that Aeetes was son of Helios the Sun who had saved Hephaestus in his chariot during the battle of the Gods and Giants.

Nobody challenged us, so we walked on into an inner courtyard, around which were many apartments. Argos described them to me:

"That one, the largest one, is where Aeetes lives with his queen Eidyia, the youngest daughter of Tethys and Oceanus. That one is for Apsyrtus, his son born to a Caucasian nymph, Asterodeia, before he married Eidyia. That one is where my mother Chalciope lives, and that one is for her younger sister Medea, who is priestess of the goddess Hecate and spends most of her time with her maidservants carrying out her duties at Hecate's temple outside the city. I expect that's where she is now.

"No she isn't!" he cried. "There she is, looking for my mother. Look, over there!"

And there was Medea. What a smasher! For a moment I forgot where we were and what we were doing. Hypsipyle was wonderful, but this Medea! The sight of her turned me upside down, if you know what I mean.

At the same time, Medea caught sight of us. I wondered if Eros might have shot an arrow at her (with any luck!), but it appeared not. She raised an eyebrow as if wondering what we were doing there. Then she seemed to recognise us, and she cried out:

"Chalciope! Come quickly! Your boys are back! Quick, come and see!"

Almost immediately her sister, followed by five of her maidservants, came rushing out of their rooms into the courtyard, and threw herself into the arms of Argos and his three brothers. Tears and sobs followed.

"I never expected to see you four back home so soon," she said eventually. "I had a feeling you were going on a fool's errand. Fancy trying to sail all the way to Greece to get your inheritances, just because old Phrixus told you to on his deathbed. I'm sure his mind was wandering at the time. I'll bet your inheritances have been squandered many times over since he flew here on that old ram of his. However, be that as it may, I'm glad you've returned safe and sound. And who are these three very handsome companions of yours?"

Argos introduced us to her, and then to Medea, who did not seem at all impressed by us. In fact she seemed rather bored, and was about to return to her rooms when Aeetes, on hearing the voice of Chalciope, came out, followed by his wife Eidyia. He gave a half-hearted welcome back to Argos and his brothers, welcomed the other three of us out of the customary politeness required to be offered to visitors, and ordered a banquet to be prepared for the evening.

Immediately there was hustle and bustle. Some of his

servants busied themselves with preparing a bull's carcass, some chopped firewood and others heated water for baths.

I had kept my eyes on Medea as much as possible since I had first caught sight of her. We were about to be invited into the quarter for guests so that we could bathe and prepare for the banquet. Medea was about to enter the door of her apartment when I saw her shudder as though hit by an arrow, spin round and stare at me. Perhaps, I thought, my dream was coming true. A young boy appeared from inside Medea's door and ran up to us.

"Which one of you is Jason?" he asked.

"I am," I replied, puzzled.

"Thank heaven I picked the right one," he laughed, and disappeared.

"What was all that about?" asked Telamon.

"I'll tell you sometime," I replied (but I never did).

Medea was staring at me without blinking. I tried to look away, but failed. I had never felt like I did then at any time before that moment, and have never felt like it again since. It was love at first sight. If you have never experienced it, you will not understand.

Eventually I had to follow my companions into the guest-rooms. But Medea and I both knew what had happened.

50

The Banquet

The banquet was a lavish affair. Somehow I had imagined that the peoples of a land so far away from Greek civilisation would indulge in a fairly primitive sort of meal. Far from it. It was certainly different from the kind of feast which I had experienced in my homeland; the meats, the vegetables and fruits and particularly the wines offered unusual tastes to my palate, but they were no less delightful.

Aeetes seemed in a jovial mood which could have been a good omen. Also I could see Medea among the ladies at the far end of the hall and I noticed that her eyes were often cast in my direction. But the time came when, after eating our fill, we were relaxing over yet another delicious wine. Suddenly Aeetes turned to face the four sons of Phrixus.

"Right then," he said. "How come you four are back here so soon after setting out on your foolhardy expedition to Greece in a futile attempt to recover your non-existent inheritances? I did warn you it was a hell of a long way. I did it myself once, but we won't go into that. Did you get shipwrecked or something? And who are these three foreigners you have brought back with you? What ship did you come back in, and where is it moored now? You, Argos, tell me the truth, since your brothers seem tongue-tied as usual."

"Well," replied Argos, "you are quite right. We were

shipwrecked, and not surprising. The captain let slip that the boat you lent us had been condemned only two weeks before we sailed."

"Nonsense," said Aeetes. "She had a good year's sailing left in her. You must have encountered a freak storm. In any case, beggars cannot be choosers. Carry on."

"We are lucky to be alive," continued Argos. "The boat fell to pieces in a storm at night. We managed to cling to one of the planks and were washed ashore on the Island of Ares. The dreadful birds of Ares there kept attacking us with their dagger-like feathers, but fortunately an expedition of heroes from Greece landed on the island and scared the birds away. They clothed and fed us and offered to bring us back here, since this land was their destination. They have also kindly offered to carry us back with them to Greece."

"You say this land was their destination," asked Aeetes. "Who are they and what do they want?"

"The king of Iolcos in Thessaly comes from the stock of Aeolus, the same stock as our father Phrixus. He swears that the whole stock of Aeolus will not escape the wrath and rage of Zeus, nor escape from the curse and vengeance due to Phrixus for the wrong planned for him by his father Athamas, until the fleece on which Phrixus escaped is returned to Greece. So he ordered his nephew Jason to form an expedition to recover it.

"Pallas Athena helped build a stout ship, the *Argo*, and Jason, aided by his friend Peleus, recruited for its crew over fifty of the noblest heroes in all Greece, and all of them descended like yourself from the immortal gods. And so, with the blessing of those gods, they have suffered many hardships and passed through many perils to get here in their quest.

"Three of their number have come with me in peace to discuss their needs with you. They are Jason, the captain of the *Argo*, son of Aeson and grandson of Cretheus who was the son of Aeolus and brother of Athamas. And Athamas, as you know, was the father of Phrixus and therefore our grandfather. Also here is Telamon, son of Aeacus, a son of Zeus himself. And last, but not least here is Augeias, a son like you of Helios the Sun himself."

"So what?" muttered Aeetes.

"They wish me to assure you," continued Argos, "that they have come here in peace and with the noblest of motives, as I have described to you, to ask you whether they may have the honour of returning the Fleece of Phrixus to its rightful home in Greece, and in return for your favour, they are willing to concentrate all their many battle talents, acquired as well as inherited from their divine ancestors, against your bitter enemies, the Sauromatae and cause them to bite the dust for your pleasure."

This was first I had heard about the Sauromatae, but, even allowing for that, I thought Argos's speech was just what was needed, and I felt glad we had picked him up on the Island of Ares. The next moment I was not so sure.

"You scoundrels," shouted Aeetes, appearing to turn red, white and blue all at the same time. "Get out of my sight, and take your trickery with you. You must think I'm stupid if you expect me to believe these warriors from Greece have come here with any intention other than seizing my sceptre and royal power. If it wasn't for the fact that you have wined and dined with me as my guests, I would tear out your tongues and hack of your hands and send you packing back to your battleship on your feet alone."

"Hold on, your majesty," I cried. "Please let me speak."

"If you must," replied Aeetes.

"We really do come in peace. We needed a crew of outstanding warriors to row and sail our ship here, because of the many fierce foes and deadly dangers we were bound to meet on our journey. But now we are here we are only too pleased to offer our services to help secure your royal power over this wonderful realm by fighting and defeating your enemies on you behalf. All that we ask in return is the Fleece of Phrixus, and we shall ensure that your royal reputation and glorious fame will be renowned throughout the whole known world."

Aeetes scowled at me through his bushy eyebrows.

"So," he continued slowly, "you reckon you are the tops, do you? Descended from the gods? Surely, then, by no means inferior to me?"

He smiled, and I felt very, very cold.

"I'll do a deal with you!" he said.

I turned slightly warmer. A deal sounded at least hopeful.

"There is a feat that I can perform, dangerous though it be, and I have yet to meet the man who can rival me. Perform this feat, and the Fleece will be yours."

"Thank you," I said. "I'll try to follow in your footsteps, however dangerous that feat may be."

I saw Medea in the distance looking very alarmed and shaking her head.

"Look me in the eyes," shouted Aeetes, "and stop staring around looking for help. You won't get any. And now listen to what you have to do.

"I have two bulls with feet of bronze which pasture on the plain of Ares, and they breathe flame from their jaws. Yoke them, plough the four-acre field and sow the furrows with some special dragons' teeth which I have. You will find that no crops grow from them but fully armed warriors, which you must slay, every one of them before they slay you. It will take you from dawn to dusk. You can rest tomorrow since it will take a day for my courtiers to prepare the field for the spectacle and seats for the spectators. And, of course, we shall hold a celebratory feast to follow the entertainment. We shall all enjoy it, I am sure, except perhaps you. So don't be late! Dawn on the day after tomorrow, on the field of Ares. Don't be late, or you may regret it."

He smiled again and this time I felt cold and stayed cold.

"Of course," he continued, "you can change your mind if you don't think you are up to the challenge. In which case, when you turn up to perform the task, I shall be watching you carefully. If you so much as shrink from getting on with it, I will make sure you never waste my time again. And you can be certain that nobody else will ever dare to challenge me again. Your companions can watch the show, and I shall be amused to watch their faces.

"So then, young hero, you and your companions here had better get back to your precious boat and your other little demi-gods, if that's what they are. Have a good day's rest tomorrow. You'll need all the strength you can muster for the day after!"

I was about to reply, but thought better of it. The seven of us rose from our couches and left the dining hall. As we did so, I caught sight of Medea. She was still staring at me. I winked at her. To my joy, she winked back!

As we walked through the courtyard, Argos told his three brothers to stay with their mother, to keep their eyes and ears open and to report anything useful. Then he joined Telamon, Augeias and me as we threaded our way through the willows of that ghostly graveyard back to *Argo* and our friends.

51

Deliberations

"Well," I said to my companions as we drew near to *Argo*, "that didn't go very well, did it?"

"You can say that again," said Telamon.

"But," said Augeias, "you did get a promise out of him. If you succeed in the feat, we can have the Fleece."

"Don't you believe it," said Argos. "I wouldn't trust Aeetes any further than I could throw him, and that's no distance at all."

"So what's the point," Telamon asked, "of Jason here trying to carry out a seemingly impossible feat if the only reward is some act of treachery from Aeetes?"

"I'll tell you," replied Argos. "Without outside help, our position is impossible. We cannot take the Fleece, however many Argonauts we are: the serpent that guards it cannot be overcome by normal means. Neither can Jason survive the fiendish feats which Aeetes has got him to agree to attempt. But there may be a solution: WITCHCRAFT!"

"Witchcraft?" responded Telamon. "How do you mean?"

"Let me explain," replied Argos. "You may not like what I have to suggest, but I believe it is our only hope. As I told you earlier today, my mother's sister, Medea, is a witch. More precisely, she is the priestess of Hecate, and is skilled in the science of sorcery. If there is anyone who can help Jason yoke the fire-breathing bulls and defeat an army of warriors and, indeed, help us to drug or distract the serpent which guards the Golden Fleece, then that person is Medea.

"Now what I suggest is that I return to the city later tonight and try to persuade my mother to ask Medea to give Jason all the help he will need. But that will not be easy. I see no reason why Medea should want to help us, but there is a slight possibility that she may do it out of love for her sister. Of course, if Medea does help Jason, it will put her into grave peril. If Aeetes even suspects Medea of treachery, he would have no hesitation in killing her."

I was sorely tempted to say what my dream and my own eyes had told me about what I suspected Medea's feelings for me might be, but I feared that I might not be believed. Indeed, I suspected my companions would think I was joking or would question my sanity. However, my spirits soared, since I suspected that Chalciope would have less trouble than expected in persuading her sister to help me.

"However," continued Argos, "I think it's worth a try. I'll return here early tomorrow morning and let you know how I got on."

By this time we had arrived at the *Argo*, hidden among the reeds. My comrades were eager to hear the news. I told them of our failure to persuade Aeetes, of his hostility and of my acceptance of his deal to surrender the Fleece if I carried out the feat of yoking the bulls and defeating the crop of warriors.

"You are not to do it!" cried Peleus. "You are our captain and we need you to lead us. I will stand in for you, even if it means death."

"No, no," cried Telamon, and then Castor and Polydeuces, and then Meleager, and then Idas, "We will stand in for you. We are warriors and that is what we are here for!"

"My friends," I responded, "thank you for your bravery, loyalty and support. But firstly, Aeetes insisted that I alone should prove my mettle. And secondly, Argos here has a plan which may very well ensure my success. Perhaps he would be kind enough to tell you about it."

And Argos described how Medea had been taught by Hecate how to handle magic herbs and incantations, how she could quench flames, subdue raging torrents, even stop the stars in their courses. He declared bravely that he had every confidence that his mother could secure her help.

And then—a miracle! At that moment the gods sent a sign. A timid dove, fleeing from a mighty hawk, fell into my lap, while the hawk impaled itself on Argus's stern-ornament, the piece which I kept knocking my head on. Mopsus immediately pronounced his interpretation of the omen.

"There can now be no question," he said, "of not carrying out Argos's plan. We must enlist the help of Medea. You must remember that Phineus told us to put our trust in the gods, particularly Aphrodite. This gentle dove here that escaped death is Aphrodite's bird. So we must call Aphrodite to our aid and accept Argos's advice."

The crew applauded. There was, however, one dissentient voice: that of Idas.

"Shame on you all!" he cried. "Are we a lot of women? Aphrodite, Argos's mother and his auntie, hawks and doves: are these what we are to call on to help us, a band of over fifty warriors from the glorious land of Greece, to recover a simple ram's fleece, guarded by a little serpent? What do you think you are?"

"Certainly not stupid," I replied, and the rest of the crew created such a din that the rest of what he said could not be heard.

When the noise subsided, I turned to Idas.

"You seem to be in a minority of one," I said.

"Sorry," he replied. "But I sometimes get the feeling my spear is redundant on this trip."

"Don't worry," I said. "It has been essential before, and may be needed again. Be patient."

Then turning to the whole crew I said, "Let Argos return now to Aea and do what he can. He will report back in the morning. Meanwhile, before we settle down to sleep for the night, we shall reverse and row a little upstream but facing downstream to moor where we can be seen, but also from where we can more quickly retire in an emergency. They know where we are anyway, and we must not seem to be lurking like cowards in a backwater."

And that is what we did.

52

Jason Alone

I slept well that night. It had been a long and emotionally exhausting day, but the wine I had imbibed at Aeetes's banquet had helped relax me. The night was moonlit and would be for several nights to come. This, I thought would be useful for us in a strange land, though we did have Argos and his brothers to guide us. Zetes and Calais were thankful for the moonlight. They spent most of the night circling round, checking for any troop movements from the Colchians but succeeding only in scaring their guards out of their slumbers. It was obvious that Aeetes did not intend anything nasty for us until after my expected humiliation on the field of Ares.

Rosy-fingered dawn was feeling her way over the Caucasian Mountains as Argos arrived hotfoot from the palace.

"Partial success!" he reported. "I spoke to my mother and she immediately approached Medea. She apparently succeeded in influencing her. Mother suspected that Medea was concerned for me and my brothers, her own nephews. After all we were obviously targets for Aeetes's wrath at the banquet. Mother also said that Medea had agonized about helping you, mainly because of the great dangers involved for her personally. But she got the impression that Medea was keen on our cause and was disgusted with the extreme brutality of her father's terms.

"Also," he said, "from what I overheard at the palace, Aeetes plans to wait until the bulls have incinerated you before stripping a whole hill of its brushwood and burning the *Argo* and all its crew as a warning to any future pirates who might try to threaten his realm. Apparently he trusts his own family, his son Apsyrtus, and his two daughters. But he has no time for Phrixus and his children, that's me and my brothers, whom he regards as foreign and treacherous upstarts. So it's just as well we've decided to throw our lot in with you and become true Argonauts."

I thought that last remark was a bit cheeky, but I kept my thoughts to myself. After all we needed extra crew for the return journey and we certainly needed them now, in view of our current perilous situation in their land.

"Thank you," I said, "for a very encouraging report. But where are your brothers now?"

"I left them behind at the palace to await developments and told them to get here as quickly as possible after learning of Medea's intentions."

I was just trying to think of something for the crew to do until the three brothers arrived when they did so, out of breath and (as usual) words. Argos leant his ear to their huffing and puffing, and eventually reported to me.

"Sorry about the delay," he said, "but they ran all the way here and were rather out-of-breath. Apparently Medea was anxious to speak to them and told them to tell you that she needs to speak to you urgently and privately. She has set out in her mule-drawn chariot, accompanied by her full complement of maidservants, two with her in the carriage and ten more following behind. Her destination is the temple of Hecate and her purpose is ostensibly to perform her customary rites to the goddess. The shrine is well concealed in a thick grove, but I know where it is, and Medea says I am to show you the way there."

"Thank you, Argos," I responded. "And thank you too, Melas, Phrontis and Cytissorus, for your speed in getting this important message through to me."

They smiled in reply, and joined the rest of the crew who resumed their breakfasting.

Peleus joined me and Argos on the quarterdeck. I explained what had happened and said that I would go with Argos immediately to meet with Medea.

"I would like to come with you as well," he said. "You need a bodyguard for the journey there."

"No," I replied. "I'll take Mopsus. I get the feeling that there may be omens which would need interpretation. Also, you're needed more here. The crew seem to be getting restless with another day of possible inactivity ahead of them. Keep them busy with maintenance work. Explain to them that I feel that we are in the hands of the gods now, and that heroic deeds and force of arms are inappropriate at present.

"My plan is as follows: We shall lie at anchor here tonight. Then early tomorrow we shall row upstream to where the river flows through the plain of Ares, ready for me to take up Aeetes's challenge and for the crew to watch and be prepared for action in the event of treachery from the Colchians. I think that's it."

"Yes, sir!" replied Peleus. "And the best of luck with Medea. At least you are unlikely to get squirted with sepia ink!"

I laughed. "I'm hoping for something rather stronger

than that to protect me from a pair of fire-breathing bulls," I said. "To be quite honest, I wish you were coming with me, but I think I must be on my own this time."

So Mopsus joined Argos and me, and we set off northwards towards the mountains, keeping Aea in the distance on our right. Argos took us along hidden paths, beside sunken streams and through dense thickets so that it was unlikely that we would be seen by Aeetes's guards. It took us several hours before Argos told us we were getting near the shrine.

Suddenly, from between the thick covering of leaves on a poplar tree by the side of our path, came the cawing of a group of chattering crows. Then the cawing ceased and one of the crows actually spoke to us. It was the voice of Hera!

"Call yourself a seer, Mopsus," she said. "Don't you realise that if two lovers meet, they will want to be alone? You and Argos should wait here. Jason must go on alone!"

Mopsus, aggrieved, mumbled, "Stone the crows, I was just going to suggest that."

The crow laughed. "No stones till we've gone, please!" and the crows disappeared as suddenly as they had appeared.

Mopsus said, "Yes, you must proceed on your own now. You will find Medea in her shrine, amenable and willing to help you. The goddess Aphrodite has come to your rescue, as Phineus foretold. Argos and I will wait here for you, in this very spot."

"Thank you both for your help and company. I must indeed proceed alone now. See you later."

And I crossed my fingers and approached the temple of Hecate.

53

I meet Medea

As I walked on alone, my thoughts were in a turmoil. What had possessed me to be thinking of making love to a witch? Moreover, to a priestess of Hecate. Hecate! I recalled what I had learnt about her at school. A primordial goddess, reputed to be followed by the hounds of hell. And yet, Medea! Why had I fallen for her, just as Peleus had fallen for Thetis? What had come over me? Was it something to do with Eros, who I knew had shot his arrow at Medea. But had he shot one at me as well? Did it matter? I was madly in love with her, and that was that. And, moreover, if Medea was going to help me in my impending ordeal, then the result could only be of benefit to the comrades for whom I was responsible. It was my duty to do everything I could to win Medea's love and sympathy and help. Even if it meant marrying her and taking her back to Iolcos with me to be…my queen!

Idle thoughts! I had to yoke fire-breathing bulls, fight countless warriors on the field of Ares, and if I survived that, I still had to snatch the Golden Fleece from the terrors of its guardian serpent. And what witch, however backed by deep sorcery, could help me do all that? But no matter. I was going to meet the woman with whom I had fallen hopelessly in love.

And suddenly I was surrounded by…eleven…no twelve maidens who ogled me alarmingly.

"I have come to meet with your mistress, Medea," I said. "I believe she is expecting me."

They giggled and pointed me in the direction of a shady grove. I found the entrance and walked in.

There, in front of the shrine stood…Medea. She was wearing a shimmering robe which sparkled with jewelled clasps, and her golden locks cascaded from beneath a silver veil down over her shapely shoulders. I shivered.

We stood there, smiling at each other, not daring to move.

I will not attempt to recount our exact words when eventually we started to speak with each other. Such love was new to us and we blushed and stuttered our way through, trying to describe in words our feelings for each other. Medea told me how she had agonised over helping me at the risk of incurring her father's wrath. I told her that if she feared to remain at home in Aeetes's palace after I had achieved success in Aeetes's challenge, then she would be welcome in Iolcos as my bride, and declared my love till death did us part. Medea thanked me for my offer and devotion, but said she would need time before she could face the decision to leave her home and loved ones.

"But," said Medea, "I must not stay here too long, or it will raise suspicions. I must give you some instructions and some magic ointment which will protect you tomorrow. This is what you must do. When you get back to *Argo* this afternoon, get two of your companions to collect the dragon's teeth from Aeetes for you to sow tomorrow."

"Why not wait until then?" I asked.

"Because, you silly," Medea replied, "tomorrow Aeetes will wait until you have yoked the bulls before he gives them to you, expecting you to be incinerated first. If you survive, he will probably give you the lot, to be on the safe side. But today, he will give you fewer teeth, thinking that, say, only one hundred warriors will be more than you can fight and not be killed by them. He values those teeth. They were a present from Athena many generations ago, and were half of those teeth from the huge dragon of Ares which Cadmus, founder of the city of Thebes, unfortunately killed. Half of those teeth were sown by Cadmus, and warriors arose from the furrows. Cadmus threw a boulder among them, and each warrior thought that another warrior had thrown it, and so they fought each other until only five of them were left. But perhaps you know that story?"

"Yes, I heard it at school," I replied, "but I didn't know that trick about throwing the boulder."

"Good," she said. "So remember it tomorrow. You may find it useful!"

"But this is even more important," she continued. "Tonight, wait until midnight. Then dress in dark clothing and take a ewe with you. Go along the riverbank until you find a spot where you will not be seen. Bathe in the running waters of the river and then dig a round pit. Prepare a pyre of wood over this pit and sacrifice the ewe whole over it. Appease the great goddess Hecate, pouring a libation of honey as you do so. Then, immediately, without looking back for any reason, leave the site and return as quickly as you can to your comrades. Sleep as well as you can, but get a friend to wake you up before dawn, so that you can anoint yourself with this ointment here."

Medea drew a small bottle from her girdle and handed it to me.

"This ointment is very powerful. It came from a plant which grew from the ichor of Prometheus when he was chained to a rock on the side of the mountains north of here. The flesh-eating eagle must have dropped some on the ground and a unique plant grew from it. The flowers were like a crocus, the root like cut flesh and the juice like the sap of a mountain-oak. Hecate led me to it and I made this ointment from it.

"You must strip completely before you spread it everywhere over your body. Leave a spot untouched and you will be vulnerable there. Need I say more?"

"I understand," I replied, blushing.

"If you do so carefully, you will not only be safe from fire and wounds, but you will feel yourself to be full of great strength and confidence. Incidentally, you should also smear your sword and spear and shield with what is left over of the ointment. But I must warn you: the spell will last only for the rest of the day. So don't go thinking that it will turn you into a lifetime superman!"

She laughed, and I was glad that, after such serious instructions, she could still be light-hearted.

"I suspect," she continued, "that Aeetes may have second thoughts about giving you the Golden Fleece if you succeed in your trials on the field of Ares. If he does, I shall have to think of something to help you. I doubt if this ointment I have given you will be strong enough to help you overcome the fearsome serpent guarding the Fleece. In any case, its effects would be wearing off by the time you get there. I suggest we tackle that problem when we meet it.

"But I really must start back to the city. My handmaidens think you have come merely to give me gifts and will wonder why it is taking so long, and Aeetes is very well aware of how long I usually take to perform my rites here at Hecate's shrine. I'll be thinking of you tonight and tomorrow as I watch you on the field of Ares. We are both in great danger, so please pray for me as well…my love."

We embraced and said our fond farewells. Medea joined her handmaidens to return to the city and I reluctantly walked away from the grove to rejoin my escort.

54

Preparations and Black Magic

As we walked back to our ship I gave Mopsus and Argos an edited account of my meeting with Medea.

Back on board, I showed my companions the magic ointment which Medea had given me and told them of her instructions. My news was well received and Mopsus declared the omens to be favourable. The Argonauts seemed pleased that obtaining the fleece would not involve them in a pitched battle with the serpent. Peleus had sent Zetes and Calais to have a quick look to assess the problem. They reported back that no way could even fifty-seven fully-armed heroes have a chance to overwhelm such a monster without massive casualties, and any attempt to do so would end in certain failure to obtain the Fleece.

Idas was still unhappy. "What's all this about ointments and magic spells and suntan lotions and other hocus-pocus?"

he asked. "I'm a warrior and thought I was in the company of warriors. What are we doing here, picking our noses and scratching our bellies? So tomorrow we shall all be watching the Jason and Medea show, admittedly hoping for success against Aeetes's sadistic challenge, but depending on his promise to give us the Fleece? And suppose he breaks his promise, and I'll bet he will. Are we going to fight the serpent like men? Apparently not. Once again we shall depend on Jason's new girlfriend to wave her magic wand. I am ashamed …"

He was howled down by the rest of the crew, all fifty-five (excluding me) of them.

When the noise subsided, Peleus walked forward and spoke: "Idas, we appreciate your frustration. But we did not come on this expedition to fight our way out of all difficulties. We are supposed to have brains as well as brawn, and we chose Jason to be our leader because he has both. What good will it be if *Argo* limps back to Greece with the Golden Fleece, but with most of the crew dead or crippled with injury? You have heard the report of Zetes and Calais concerning the serpent which was obviously chosen as the guardian of the Fleece for its invincibility. If you want convincing, go and have a look for yourself. Go on! The serpent lives on this south side of the river. If you are not back by nightfall, we shall assume he has strangled you in his coils."

"No thanks," said Idas. "I'll go along with the rest of you if I must."

I addressed the crew: "Thank you all for your confidence in me. I cannot promise you success, but the plan I have outlined to you seems to be the one most likely to succeed.

I have chosen Telamon and Aethalides to fetch the dragon's teeth from Aeetes."

They set off on their mission. I had chosen Aethalides as a companion for Telamon because he was the famous son of Hermes, and was the expedition's official herald.

And so we prepared for our evening meal, and made our sacrifices to Hera. Telamon and Aethalides returned with the dragon's teeth soon after we had started eating. The crew were keen to see the teeth.

"Nasty looking things, aren't they?" commented Peleus. "Let's hope the warriors they grow into are an improvement!"

As midnight approached, the good ship *Argo* vibrated to the snores of fifty-four Argonauts. I had ordered Zetes and Calais to fly around on guard duty, but on no account to follow me.

I had been on many midnight foraging expeditions while I was at Cheiron's wonderful school, and had thought nothing of being on my own at the dead of night. But this was different. I was not looking forward to my task at all. I would not have minded so much if the rites were for some goddess other than Hecate. But Hecate! I confess I was frightened, but there was no sensible alternative but to carry out Medea's instructions. It was that or face death on the field of Ares.

I covered myself in a dark cloak, one which Hypsipyle had given me as a parting present. I suppose it was inappropriate, but it was the only dark garment available. I took with me some milk and a honeycomb and a ewe, all of which Argos had obtained from a friendly farm near where *Argo* was moored.

The night sky was blanketed with patchy cloud beneath a watery moon which provided a ghostly aspect to the Colchian countryside. I staggered westward along the north side of the river, away from the city, until I found a depression in the riverbank where my grisly task would be hidden from view. I tethered the ewe and I plunged naked into the river where I washed my body thoroughly. Then I dug a round pit three feet deep and piled up some billets of wood over it. Next I sacrificed the ewe on the pile, set light to the wood and poured libations mingled with milk and honey over the flames. I was trembling when I called on Hecate to help me in the impending contest on the field of Ares.

It worked. I heard rumblings from deep in the ground beneath my feet and I sensed the approach of the dread goddess arising from the abyss. I did not hang about. As I ran away, not daring to look back, I sensed the hissing of countless snakes, saw the reflections on the grass of countless torches behind me, and heard the baying of the hounds of Hell straining to follow me. The whole meadow trembled beneath my feet, and I heard the terrified shrieks of the nymphs that haunted the marsh and river as I ran beside them.

I did not stop until I reached the *Argo*. Peleus was waiting anxiously for my return.

"How did you get on?" he asked.

I outlined my experiences and he whistled.

"This Medea," he said, "you say she is the priestess of this goddess Hecate?"

"I'm afraid so," I replied. "But somebody has to do the job, I suppose. Anyway, if Medea was not her priestess, it would not be possible for her to help us. I hope that when we get back to Greece, she may not feel the need to continue with such extreme sorcery."

Peleus was about to comment, but instead said:

"Get some sleep now. I'll wake you up an hour before dawn so that you can protect yourself with that magic ointment of hers."

"Thanks," I said, and promptly went to sleep.

Peleus woke me up as he had promised and I jumped down onto the riverbank and I stripped naked once more. It was getting a little tedious, I must confess. I applied the ointment everywhere on my body, leaving no accessible nook or cranny untreated. I pride myself in being thorough when the occasion demands. I also spread the stuff over my sword and spear and shield as Medea had instructed. Then I climbed back on board.

Peleus laughed. "You look as though you've just run all the way here from Greece," he said. "I was afraid the stuff might turn you a funny colour, like sepia, and give the game away when Aeetes sees you today, but you just look very sweaty."

We chatted as dawn crept cautiously over the Caucasian mountains, and shed light on the day of reckoning.

55

Fire-breathing bulls and bloody battle

I expect you think we would have rowed *Argo* to the site
of the contest at crack of dawn. We did not. We had
breakfast first, since I insisted that my army of Argonauts
should be well fed and in peak condition in case they were
needed to fight the Colchians.

Nor did we leave immediately after breakfast. The crew
were anxious to try out me and my weapons for invincibility,
and I invited them to do so. Peleus punched me in the
stomach and got a blast of wind in his face for his pains
(I bandaged his hand up for him later). Then Idas whacked
my spear with his mighty sword which received a nasty nick
in its blade. He then tried to pierce my shield with the same
sword and he bent its tip very badly.

"Very well," Idas said. "You win. Now I shall have to
sharpen my sword's blade and straighten its tip. But you
may still need my services before we get back home.
And...er...good luck today in the contest."

All this did something to cheer me. I gave orders for
Argo to be released from its mooring and rowed backwards
and upstream against the current to the site of the impending
contest. Apparently the field of Ares stretched from the
city of Aea, east of the sepulchral grove of willows, down
to the River Phasis and then continued from its south bank
in a large sweep, containing in its folds the grove of Ares
where dwelt the serpent which guarded the Golden Fleece.

We moored on the north bank of the river, facing across the field towards the city.

We could see stands had been erected on the far side of the site, and already they were being filled by Colchian spectators. The central stand was of an imposing appearance, festooned with royal flags and billowing bunting. I ordered my crew to arrange themselves, some on the riverbank and others behind them on the *Argo*, so that they could be seen to watch the spectacle in opposition to the Colchians. I told them they would have to cheer mightily since they were heavily outnumbered, and they assured me they would do their best.

Then we heard trumpets sounding as Aeetes approached to take up his place in the royal box. He was wearing a purple robe over the stiff cuirass which Ares had given him and on his head was a golden helmet with four plumes. He was wielding a shield made from numerous hides and a fearsome spear, both reputed to be unconquerable. It was no wonder he could claim to have yoked the bulls and fought the bull's-teeth warriors single-handed and with success. And he arrived in a stately chariot drawn by amber-coloured horses, surrounded by crowds of his followers.

As soon as he had taken his place, I leapt from the *Argo* and walked into the centre of the arena, holding my spear and shield and with my sword swinging from my shoulder. I noted that the plough and the yoke had been placed on the ground ready for me. I remembered that Argos had told me that this plough was fashioned from one piece of solid adamant and had been forged by Hephaestus; it was a mighty piece of machinery. A square of four acres around me had been identified by markers and I knew that these must be the acres which I was to furrow and sow with the dragon's teeth which I carried in my helmet. I also took note of several boulders at the edge of the marked-out area, and I earmarked the largest as the one which I might need to use as Medea had suggested.

I was ready, but where were the bulls? I heard a snorting noise behind me. I turned quickly and there they were, two of the brutes. Hephaestus had surpassed himself: from their mouths of bronze shot sheets of flame which I estimated were twenty-one feet long. I was tempted to avoid the flames by circling the beasts and attempting to tackle them from the side or rear. But courage swelled within me. I remembered my days on the farm at Cheiron's school, and, ignoring the fireworks, I simply walked up to the right-hand bull, grasped the tip of its horn and dragged it near the yoke of bronze. Then, kicking its bronze foot with my boot, I forced it down on to its knees. The left-hand bull charged me but I knocked it down with a single blow, and held them both down on their fore-knees. Castor and Polydeuces (I had instructed them previously) rushed up and, avoiding the flames, handed me the yoke.

"That's cheating!" cried Aeetes from his stand.

"Nonsense!" I shouted in reply, as the twins hurried back to the ship, trailing smoke from their smouldering clothes. I bound the yoke tightly to the bulls' necks, lifted the bronze pole between them and fastened it to the yoke. I slung my shield on my back and hitched my helmet which contained the dragon's teeth to my belt, ready to sow them. I used my spear to prick the bulls on their flanks. They appeared to sense who was boss, and off we went, starting to plough the four acres. The bulls seemed to have run out of fuel: the flames diminished and the heat was off.

I heard a cry of dismay from the direction of Aeetes's stand. He obviously had not expected me to survive this far. But the contest was far from being finished. The crop from the sowing was still to come.

Up and down the four acres we went, churning the smooth ground into great furrows. It was slow work and heavy going, but I did not feel at all tired. Medea's magic had worked well. I thought it best to leave sowing the teeth until the area was half ploughed. Then I threw a few teeth as far away as possible into the clods of the previous furrows to test their effect. I watched carefully as I continued ploughing and was amazed to see the result. Nothing happened and nothing did happen even when I had finished all the ploughing and had sown all one hundred teeth.

I freed the bulls who seemed glad to wander off to graze far away from me on the plain, their energy greatly diminished. I wandered back to the ship to the cheers of the crew and was handed a helmet full of fresh water, which I emptied. It had been thirsty work.

Peleus suddenly exclaimed, "Don't look now, but the crop is starting to sprout!"

I did 'look now'. The area I had ploughed was beginning to bristle with sturdy shields, double-pointed spears and glistening helmets. Inside were battle-ready warriors looking round for someone to fight. Already there were twenty-three fully formed warriors who saw me as I approached and drew their swords. There was no time to lose. I hurried towards the giant boulder which I had previously earmarked and tried to lift it. It needed all my strength and concentration but I succeeded. I started running and using my last reserve of effort I hurled it into the midst of the advancing army, which by now had numbered forty-seven. They stopped in their tracks. Three of them were instantly crushed into the ground as the rock came to earth. The others were filled first with alarm and then with fury. Each warrior apparently blamed the others around them and slashed out at them with their swords. Arms were severed, heads rolled down the furrows and newly arrived warriors slithered and squelched in the blood which began to cover the whole field. I stayed at the edge of the conflict until all one hundred had arrived and ninety-five had been crushed or slaughtered. The remaining five were looking round them in a kind of daze and I suspected that they were beginning to smell a rat. I despatched them while they hesitated. My sword and shield were certainly not to be argued with, and I thanked Medea's magic for that.

I staggered back to the *Argo*. By now I was so weary that I almost failed to notice the cheers of my loyal crew.

"Well done!" said Peleus as I sat down to rest on the quarterdeck.

"What's going on among the Colchian stands?" I asked.

"Not a lot," replied Peleus. "When they saw what was happening to the warriors, they all packed up and drifted back to the city."

I looked back over the battlefield and saw that he was right. Not a body could be seen anywhere, except, of course, the dismembered remains of the dragon's-teeth army.

I gave a command for the crew to row the *Argo* to the opposite, south, bank of the Phasis, still keeping our prow facing downstream. I thought we would be safer there from any treacherous attack from Aeetes and his cronies. They would have to cross the river to get at us, and I was not aware of any bridge or ford in the vicinity. To be on the safe side, I asked Zetes and Calais to assume sentry duty, and they seemed glad of a chance to stretch their wings once again.

I fell into a deep sleep and Peleus ordered the rest of the crew to try to do the same.

56

The Golden Fleece

It was some time after midnight when Ancaeus shook me.

"Wake up," he said. "There's somebody calling to us from the riverbank opposite."

I listened and Argos (backed by his brothers) whispered to me that they thought it was Medea's voice. I cupped my hand to my ear and listened.

I heard a voice crying, "Quickly, quickly, come and get me!" It was Medea's voice.

I gave orders to cast off and row to the opposite bank. Ancaeus had some difficulty sorting out the rowing-crew and I cursed them for their unpreparedness.

"Where are you?" I shouted as softly as I could. Medea sensibly kept repeating, "Here, here!" so that we could correct our course across the river in the dark. But soon we saw a gleam through the gloom. Medea had some magic phosphorescent charm which glowed with a golden light and we soon reached her.

I climbed over the railings on the quarterdeck and jumped down on to the riverbank. Argos and his brothers joined me. Medea ran up to us and embraced me.

"Please," she cried, "you must save me, my beloved. And you must save yourselves too! Aeetes has discovered everything. There is no time to lose. We must row downstream quietly to get the Golden Fleece, and then reach the open sea as soon as we can. I'll show you the way."

We, all six of us, climbed back on board and I ordered Ancaeus to cast off and row downstream.

On board, Medea explained: "As soon as dawn appears Aeetes plans to swarm down to this river with all his guards. There is a bridge about a mile upstream and he will split his forces there and move westward along the two banks so that he can attack *Argo* on whichever bank it is moored. He thinks he will catch you all asleep. I had to use my magic to slip unseen out of the palace and the city gates and find my way here in the dark. We have no time to lose. Fortunately a moon is just rising which, in spite of the clouds, will give us enough light to find our way to the oak grove where the Golden Fleece is guarded by the sleepless serpent. Trust me and I will lead you there and help you get the Fleece from it."

"But," she continued, "you must make me a solemn promise. I have risked everything to help you in your contest on the field of Ares. Now I can never return here while Aeetes lives, and I must rely on your promise to marry me and take me back with you to Greece."

I assured her of my love and swore by Olympian Zeus and Hera, the queen of marriage, that, when we were back at my home, I would take her as my own wedded wife.

Medea guided Ancaeus to where, on the south bank, there was a lawn called the Ram's Bed, since it was there that the ram that carried Phrixus landed. We moored against the riverbank there. Medea and I jumped down and she guided me southwards. A fresh-risen moon was reflecting a ghostly light down from the underbelly of low clouds. I jumped when I knocked my shin against the base of an altar which, Medea explained, Phrixus had once set up to honour Zeus, the help of fugitives, when he sacrificed the golden ram at the bidding of Hermes.

"I hope you are not accident-prone," said Medea as I nursed my shin.

"Certainly not," I replied. "Where is this sacred grove, then?"

"We're in it," Medea replied. "Your night-vision isn't very good, is it?"

"It's been good enough in the past," I replied rather tersely. "So where is the oak with the Golden Fleece?"

"Behind you, my love," she replied. "Mind that serpent's coil!"

I turned quickly and nearly jumped out of my skin. There, almost above my head twirled one of the many coils of an horrendous serpent. I retreated just as it tried to curl round me. It was no wonder even an hundred Argonauts could not have fought it. Its huge main body was covered with hard, dry scales like armour-plating and from it waved a long neck ending in a head topped with a golden crest and sporting jaws with countless teeth, a three-forked tongue and spiral fangs. But the many coils which also grew from its torso were the most alarming: they whirled and twirled menacingly, ready to crush anything and anybody who dared to approach within their reach. All in all, a thoroughly nasty piece of work.

Within this complex of nastiness and surrounded by it on three sides was an oak tree on the top of which was…the Golden Fleece! At last, there it was.

"It's a bit small," I commented to Medea.

"Well, what did you expect?" she replied. "One the size of an ox-hide? It was only a ram, for heaven's sake."

"What I meant," I said, "was…well, never mind. How do we get at it?"

"Leave it to me," she replied.

Medea stared the serpent straight in its eyes and called on Sleep, that most powerful of all the gods, to charm the monster. She called to the queen of the underworld to help her in her task. And it worked. The coils relaxed and the horrid head rolled sideways. Its three-forked tongue and fangs flopped feebly forward and its jaws snapped shut on them. This seemed to revive the brute, which caused me some alarm, but Medea seized a newly cut spray of juniper, added it to a brew which she had brought with her and sprinkled the mixture into the serpent's eyes. Slowly the beast continued to relax until its whole structure collapsed to fill the grove with a vast complex of coils, topped by a somnolent neck and head.

"Come on!" cried Medea. "Climb up and get the Fleece before it wakes up!"

I did so and there I was, returning to the *Argo*, with the Golden Fleece on my back, followed closely by Medea. Dawn was already casting its early shadows across the field as I climbed back on board to the cheers of the crew. Even Idas looked pleased. Now that the early rays of the sun began to reflect from its golden tufts, I was more impressed by it.

The whole crew wanted to touch it, but there was no time to be lost. I stored it safely under the planks of the quarterdeck and insisted that Medea should to hide there with it. I gave orders to cast off. Ancaeus already had thirty of the crew ready to row with twenty more ready to give protection to all with their ox-hide shields. The rest of us (except Ancaeus of course) were to use our bows and arrows as best we could. We expected to be shot at from either bank. Off we went downstream, heading for the open sea. We had several miles to go and we were not a minute too soon.

Our speed, even with thirty-oar power, could not match the speed of the horses of Aeetes's guards. I looked back from the quarterdeck and saw his army charging at full speed along both sides of the river. Within minutes they had caught up with us.

I could see Aeetes leading his forces on the north bank. He was in a magnificent chariot with his son Apsyrtus at the reins of two fine horses, swift as the blasts of the wind, and which Medea told me later were a gift to Aeetes from Helios, the Sun-god, his father. In his left hand he held a round shield and in the other a huge pine-torch and his mighty spear was by his side, pointing forward, ready for instant use. I aimed an arrow at him and so did three of my crew, but to no effect: the arrows simply bounced off his shield.

I could see that he was in full fury. He was shouting curses on us and threatening his followers with dire punishment if they failed to stop us reaching the sea.

Soon we were showered with arrows from both banks, but our shields warded off most of them; others pierced the woodwork of *Argo*, but none injured the crew. Ancaeus steered a steady course midstream, and, as we reached the mouth of the estuary, Aeetes and his army had to peel right and left amid horrifying cries of frustration that they had failed to stop us. They had been tricked by Medea, one of their royal household, and had lost their treasured possession—the Golden Fleece. I almost felt sorry for them.

And so we were out on the open sea. I rushed to the rear of the quarterdeck to check that we were not being followed by any warship of Aeetes and collapsed, unconscious.

When I came round, I was lying on the deck with my head in Medea's lap. She was bathing a large lump on the front of my head with a sweet-smelling salve from a little pouch which she kept attached to her girdle.

Peleus was looking at me. I asked him what had happened.

"When you rushed to the rear of the deck," he replied, "you knocked your head once more on Argus's new stern-ornament. I'm getting worried about you. You're definitely getting accident-prone. How many times have you knocked your head on that damned ornament since we left the clashing rocks?"

"I've no idea," I replied irritably.

"And you are becoming innumerate too," he said as he wandered off to control the *Argo* for me while I was temporarily indisposed.

I wanted to throw something at him, but I was much too comfortable lying there with Medea murmuring sweet nothings to me and soothing my brow.

57

Home at last!

Here in the Elysian Fields, you might imagine that we have no problems. Not so.

I was just about to start a detailed account of our journey home to Greece, a journey I may add which has been subjected to more false accounts than the number of times I knocked my head on Argus's unnecessary stern-piece, when my medium gave me an ultimatum:

"I'm getting tired," he said, "and you can have only five more chapters. You've gone on for long enough. Just look at this chapter. The fifty-seventh! My word-processor needs a rest. And so do I. And so do your readers, if you've got any left by now. Enough is enough. Five more chapters and that is it. Absolutely it. And no cheating by making each chapter longer than usual. You know what we agreed. Each chapter to be no longer than a bedtime reader can read aloud without saying 'that's enough for tonight, dear' before the end of it, or more than his listener can hear before nodding off."

He does go on so, sometimes. Not a happy medium. So I shall have to skip details of our journey home. Perhaps some other time. But I have five chapters left to give you some account of the end of my story.

There we were one afternoon, scudding up the gulf of Pagasae before a superb southerly.

Peleus seemed almost sorry to be nearly home.

"I think," he said, "that when we've seen that your parents are all right and we've sorted out old Pelias, I'll have a spell teaching back at the old school. I reckon Cheiron will be glad of a teacher with some extra experience. And, of course, there's the nipper, Achilles. I expect he's grown some."

"You can't fool me," I said. "I can tell that you are quite excited really. You know I think my father may have died by now, and you're trying to put me at ease."

"Please yourself, my lad," he said, "but I think it's best to look on the bright side if possible."

And there, straight ahead, was Pagasae, the place whence we had sailed many moons ago. I was somewhat disappointed not to see a welcoming party on the beach, but I told myself that possibly we were all presumed dead. Certainly Pelias never expected to see us again, and, if the truth were known, nor did anyone else, though they may have expressed some hope for our survival.

Anyway, there we were beached at Pagasae, and we drew dear old *Argo* out of the water using the same rollers we had used to launch her. The crew were in great spirits, glad to be home again. Argus was fussing around inspecting *Argo*'s underside like an old hen checking her chickens.

"Perfect," he kept saying. "Perfect. Almost like new! You don't get craftsmanship like that in foreign parts, young Argos," he said to the eldest son of Phrixus. "*Argo* would not have fallen to bits like your ship did in the Black Sea!"

"It wasn't my ship," replied Argos. "It was an old wreck that Aeetes wanted to get rid of."

"That's not the point," said Argus. "My point is ..."

I decided to interrupt their conversation and address the crew.

"My friends," I said. "Fellow Argonauts. We have made it at last. Here we are with the Golden Fleece, returned to its true home for the glory and prosperity of Greece. Congratulations to you all!

"Now what I suggest is this: whether or not my dear father is still alive, you are all very welcome at my family palace for a celebratory feast and party. I propose, in view of the uniqueness of the occasion, that this continue for at least two weeks to give all your friends and relations time to come and join us in our thanksgivings to the blessed gods who looked after our interests so well during our adventures. I know this will put the resources and accommodation of the palace to severe strain, to put it mildly, but what of that? We must send out messengers from the palace to spread the news of our return and invite your nearest and dearest to come and join us in our celebrations and see the Golden Fleece with their own eyes. So pick up your gear and follow me up the hill to the palace."

A great cheer followed my speech and before I could protest, they put the Golden Fleece on my back and lifted me on to the shoulders of Castor and Polydeuces as we set off for my father's home.

Soon hundreds of townsfolk, who must have spotted our arrival, poured down the hill to cheer us and join in the procession.

"Your father is still alive!" one of them shouted. It was true. When we arrived at the gates of the palace, my mother had come out to greet and embrace me with floods of tears.

"Yes, dear," she said at last, as we walked arm in arm into the palace, "your father is still alive but very old and weak, but he was determined to stay alive to see your return. He had great faith that you would return with all these friends of yours, and with the Golden Fleece as well. Isn't it beautiful? Too good for that wretch Pelias. Why don't you get your friends to stay here and invite their relatives to join them? We could have a bit of a party and keep the lovely Fleece here with us for a few weeks before we let him have it, couldn't we dear? Oh it's so lovely to have you home again safe and sound. You must be very tired, and need a really good rest. But first you must come and let your dear father see you. Oh, here's the door. Why don't you go in on your own? I'll go and get things organised for all your friends, because they must be very tired too. See you later, dear," and off she toddled.

I opened the door of my father's room and went inside, closing it behind me. The expression of joy on his face was a sight for sore eyes.

"Well done, lad," he said. "Well done, but who is this with you?"

I thought that his poor mind must be wandering, so I asked him whether I had two heads.

"My body," he replied, "may be infirm, but my brain is not. I repeat, who is this with you?"

I looked behind me. Medea was standing there, smiling.

"Th...th...th...this is Medea, my wife," I replied.

"Pleased to meet you," said my father. "You must be old Aeetes's youngest. Did you have a good trip here?"

"Yes, thank you," said Medea. "I hope I shall prove to be a good daughter-in-law to you."

"I am sure you will try your best," said father, "and I have heard that you possess the ability to achieve your objectives. But you must both join your friends. You have much to celebrate. There will be plenty of time in the coming weeks for us to chat some more. I am tired now, and wish to sleep."

We left the room and I asked Medea how she had got into father's room. Indeed, I had not set eyes on her since we had disembarked from the *Argo*.

"Darling," she said, "I saw you had a lot to do, so I thought I would keep a low profile until things had settled down and I could meet your family and palace people at greater leisure."

"But," I replied, "did you not see my mother as I walked through the palace with her?"

"Of course I did," she replied, "but she did not see me. However, I was keen to meet your father. If he was stronger and younger, would he not be able to help you by backing your claim to the throne of Iolcos?"

"I would love to see him stronger and younger," I replied, "but only for his own sake and happiness."

Medea gave me a strange look and said, "I'll see what can be arranged."

58

Medea and Aeson

The evening was spent in riotous partying. We all awoke next morning with sore heads and foul tongues.

Medea left our bed early as I was trying to focus my eyes on her. She said she would be away for nine days, flying in her dragon-drawn chariot round all the mountains of Greece and most other places, collecting the herbs and plants she required to produce a drug which would knock forty years off of my father's life.

I was in no state to argue. She said, "See you later, darling!" and disappeared. She was true to her word: nine days she said and nine days she meant.

I explained her absence by saying that she had gone to visit relatives, but I do not think I was believed. However, we all had a whale of a time celebrating anything we could think of. Relatives and friends of the crew kept coming and on the eighth day there were actually two hundred and ninety-three of us (excluding palace staff) packed into every nook and cranny of the palace (and stables!) at night-time. Food and wine were brought in abundance by the visitors, for which my mother was very grateful.

Acastus was the only Argonaut who visited Iolcos to see his father. He reported that Pelias was very angry because we still had the Golden Fleece at Aesonis but even more so (Acastus suspected) because we had returned at all. However, Acastus had told his father that we intended to visit him with the Fleece once the celebrations were over, and that seemed to appease him.

Then Medea returned and said she had been successful in acquiring the required ingredients for her magic concoction. That night, when the halls and stables were reverberating to the snores of wine-drenched warriors, she asked me to drag my father's bed to a secluded spot behind the kitchen-garden. There she made me help her set up two turf-built altars, one to Hecate and the other to Youth. We dug two trenches nearby and she sacrificed a black-faced sheep over them, letting the blood pour down into them. As she poured libations of milk and wine, she chanted sinister spells, calling up the spirits from the earth and praying to the king of shades and his stolen queen to preserve Aeson's spirit in his body. Using spells she relaxed his body and arranged it quite tenderly over a blanket of herbs.

At this point Medea asked me to leave because the uninitiated were prohibited from witnessing the mystic rites. Since it was my father who was in her hands, I asked if an exception might be made in my case. After some thought she agreed saying that my presence could be a preliminary to my initiation, and that she intended to make me a priest of Hecate in due course. I had no such intention, but I pretended to agree so that I could continue to keep an eye on my father.

Medea circled round the blazing altars, her hair streaming behind her. She dipped her torches in the black blood of the trenches, set fire to them and placed them on the altars. Thrice she cleansed my father's body with fire, thrice with water, thrice with sulphur. While this was going on, a cauldron was bubbling away, frothing and foaming.

In went the ingredients she had gathered during her nine-day grand tour:

- roots, seeds, flowers from Thessalian valleys,
- stones from the far east,
- sands washed by the tides of Oceanus,
- hoar frosts gathered by the light of a full moon,
- flesh and wings of a screech-owl,
- entrails of a werewolf,
- scales of a slender water-snake,
- stag's liver (stags live to a great age),
- eggs and head of a nine-generation-old crow,
- hundreds and thousands (of other nameless ingredients).

Medea stirred this concoction thoroughly with a withered branch of an olive tree. As she did so, the branch gradually grew leaves, then clusters of olives. Sometimes the mixture bubbled over and spilt on the ground. Where this happened, the earth grew green, the grass and flowers appeared.

"It works!" she cried, and before I could stop her, she drew out a knife from her girdle and slit my father's throat. But as the blood seeped out, she poured ladles-full of the concoction from the cauldron on to the cut and the blood ceased flowing out and the mixture started seeping in. And she opened his mouth and poured more of the mixture in there as well.

Gradually my father's hair and beard changed colour from white to ginger. His wrinkles smoothed out, flesh filled his sagging dew-laps, his limbs filled out with sinew and his pot belly became flat.

The new, young Aeson arose from his bed and Medea led him gently indoors, leaving me to clear up the mess. Later that night, I went in to see my father, who now looked more like a brother.

"What in hell do you think you two have been up to?" he thundered. "I don't want to be young again. All I wanted, after a long life, was to see you safe home again, and then die peacefully in my bed. Now I shall probably outlive my dear wife by very many long and lonely years. I wish you had consulted me first before you let your wife, however well-intentioned, loose on me."

I didn't know what to say. I sat down by his side and held his hand.

"Don't worry about it, son," he said. "What's done is done, and I'll have to make the best of it. You meant well. That comforts me."

I joined Medea in our bedroom.

"I think your father is not too happy," she said. "But never mind. He will enjoy his newfound youth eventually and be a great comfort to us when we are King and Queen of Iolcos. Trust me, my darling. Soon I will make sure all will be as it should be. You need some sleep. Goodnight!"

She turned over in bed and went to sleep. But I was not happy with how things were developing.

59

Medea and Pelias

Late next morning when I awoke, Medea had disappeared again.

Peleus breezed in for a chat.

"Your dad looks fantastic! He's just joined us for breakfast and your mum is wandering around in floods of tears. I think she will take some time to get used to him. I suppose it was all Medea's doing, I mean, making him younger and all that. I looked for you during the night but could not find you anywhere. I presume you were outside somewhere performing some hocus-pocus."

"Something like that," I replied. "But have you seen Medea? She's wandered off again."

"Ah," said Peleus. "Zetes and Calais came back just now from their early morning fly-about and reported seeing Acastus and Medea wandering off in the direction of Iolcos. I expect they are up to something."

"It's all very worrying," I said. "Somehow I don't feel in control any more. Medea is a very loving wife, but sometimes I think she is rather too loving, if you know what I mean."

Peleus smiled.

"Well," I continued, "what do you think I should do about it?"

"Not a lot," he replied. "I don't think I am the one to ask for marriage guidance. If you remember, I married a maritime goddess and now you have married a witch. What were we to expect except problems?"

"You are a great help," I said.

"I do my best," he said as he wandered back to breakfast.

I badly needed to do something physical to relax my mind from its current tension. I suggested to Peleus after breakfast that we go foraging in the woods behind the palace. He agreed readily and we set off with our gear and oak staffs. When we got to a clearing at the top of a hill, we remembered how, years ago, we had sparred each other with our staffs on our way to Cape Sepias. We repeated our tussle and again found that we were fairly evenly matched. This pleased us a great deal, and we returned to the palace late in the afternoon with our bags well filled with game.

Our euphoria was short-lived. Medea returned from Iolcos early in the evening. She passed us on her way to our bedroom.

"I'm exhausted," she said. "I simply must get some sleep, darling. I've sorted everything out for us. Pelias is dead. I'll tell you all about it tomorrow. Goodnight!"

Peleus and I stood there gobsmacked. I was about to run after her, demanding immediate details and explanations, despite her dubious exhaustion, when Acastus arrived in what we could see was a more credible state of exhaustion.

He collapsed on to a couch and called for wine. We would not let him speak until we were reasonably sure he had recovered.

"We know," I said to him, "that your father is dead. Medea has told us. She arrived back here ahead of you. We are very sorry. Please tell us what happened when you feel fit to do so."

"I still cannot believe what happened," he said eventually. "I expect you heard that Medea and I went to Iolcos this morning to visit my father. We saw Zetes and Calais circling round overhead and they must have seen us. Medea said she had a suggestion to put to my father which would be to his advantage and asked me to accompany her so that I could introduce her to my father and my sisters. I readily agreed because I was keen to see my father again and become reconciled to him. He was not too pleased that I had joined the expedition in the first place.

"Anyway, when we got to Iolcos, we entered the palace and the first people we met were my four sisters, Pisidice, Pelopia, Hippothoe and Alcestis. Medea told them how she had fallen out with Jason and begged for asylum with Pelias's court. This was news to me, because, from what I have seen since we left Colchis, you and Medea seemed to be getting on so well. However..."

"We have not fallen out," I interrupted. "Medea was making it up. Please continue."

"Well," he went on, "my sisters took a liking to her and then Medea told them how she had just made your father regain his youthful vigour by using her magic spells and how you had not appreciated it one little bit. They told Medea how old and frail their father Pelias had become and wondered if Medea could do something for him. She hesitated, saying it was not an easy thing to do and that she would have to think about it. The more she hesitated, the more they implored her to try, and eventually she agreed, though reluctantly.

"She said she would like them to see an experiment first, because she said she wanted them to be really certain that they wished to go ahead with the process. They agreed and she asked them to obtain a really old ram from our father's flock, and for a cauldron of boiling water. When these arrived, Medea cut the ram's throat, plunged it into the pot and threw in a few handfuls of her magic herbs. A few minutes later we heard a bleating sound and suddenly a lamb jumped from the pot and ran off down the corridor.

"My sisters were really impressed, and urged Medea to repeat the procedure for Pelias, though Alcestis said she was uncertain and would rather opt out.

"So the other three sisters, Medea and I went to Pelias's rooms, and Medea was introduced to him. He seemed very impressed by her, having heard of her reputation as a sorceress and said she was very wise not to want to have anything more to do with that upstart Jason."

"Pardon?" I said.

"I'm simply quoting what he said. As the minutes went by, I noticed that Pelias and his courtiers were looking very sleepy. In fact, after another few minutes they were all snoring away on their couches. We asked Medea what was wrong, and she explained that she had drugged them with one of her spells. She asked again for a cauldron of boiling water to be brought and asked me and my sisters to lift Pelias from his couch on to a table. Then she threw more handfuls of something (it looked like sand) into the boiling water.

"I too, like Alcestis, was having second thoughts by now, though I genuinely believed she had the power to rejuvenate my father. However, I said I would rather be disassociated with the rest of it. Medea called me a cissy, and told my three sisters to show me what stuff they were made of. 'Come on girls,' she cried. 'Get your knives out and slit his throat!' They were pale and trembling as they did so, and Medea poured some boiling mixture on to the wound and into his mouth. 'Now hack him to bits,' she cried, 'and throw them into the pot!' They did so and collapsed with terror on to the empty couch.

"I stared at the pot, praying for my father to climb out of it. He didn't. I looked round to ask Medea what had gone wrong, but she was nowhere to be seen. I rushed to the window and looked out. I saw her nearly a mile away, hurrying back here. I ran out and followed her but I could not catch her up. Where is she?"

"Resting," I said. "But calm down, please do. There's nothing we can do now. If I had known this was going to happen, I would have done everything I could to prevent it. I have married a woman whose powers I cannot control and whose mind and emotions I cannot comprehend. I cannot find words to say how sorry I am that your father is dead. I must be honest and say that I did not admire him. I think he was a cruel tyrant and unfit to be king. But he was your father and deserved respect for that.

"You will appreciate that this is as much a blow to me as it was for you. Please will you give me a short while to consider what I must do next. I promise I shall give you my decision very soon."

"Yes," said Acastus. "I can see that you are now in a difficult position. Please take your time."

I did take my time. I needed to. Peleus asked if I needed him to share my thoughts with. I thanked him but said that this was something I had to do alone. I considered whether

I should bring Medea into the arena because she was my wife, but I decided against it.

I wandered into the kitchen garden where I could be alone with my thoughts. About an hour later I returned to the main hall where Acastus and Peleus were sitting and talking.

"I have come to a decision," I said to Acastus. "My wife has in effect murdered your father the king and there is now no place for her in this part of the country. My duty is to be with her and we shall go to live in Corinth, which is the native city of her father, Aeetes, who was given its kingdom by his father Helios, the Sun-god, before he left for Colchis.

"It is only right then that you should succeed your father as king of Iolcos and I hereby renounce all my rights inherited from my father, Aeson, to that throne. You must take the Golden Fleece with you and secure it safely in your palace. May you and all Thessaly, indeed all Greece, prosper through its possession. Guard it well.

"I leave my father and mother behind me here in Aesonis and I am sure you will respect their independence and safety. I know my father is now young in body but I am sure he is still old in wisdom, and can give you sound advice should you need it. As for your poor sisters, do not blame them for what they did. Medea misled them and they acted as they did out of love for your father. I wish you well."

Acastus stood up, came to me and we embraced. "Thank you, Jason," he said.

"You are a damned fool, Jason." It was Medea's voice. She came out from behind a pillar and had obviously heard everything.

"However," she continued, "I quite like the sound of Corinth. We shall go to live there if we must."

60

Escape to Corinth

I had a bright idea. Why not sail to Corinth in the *Argo*? I calculated that there were eighteen Argonauts who came from the Peloponnese, and a further ten from Attica, Boeotia and Aetolia, which were down south that way. If they rowed the boat to Corinth, they would be well on their way home.

Next morning I called an assembly of all those present, Argonauts, relatives and hangers-on. I explained fully what had happened and of my decisions. I think they were somewhat sad that I would not be king of Iolcos, but they all knew that the Argonauts' success in bringing back the Golden Fleece would be celebrated throughout Greece for countless generations to come. Their pedigree had been established. They thanked me for that.

As for rowing the *Argo* to Corinth, they couldn't wait. I would have thought they had had enough, but they said they wanted the glory. In fact, fourteen of those who came from places nowhere near Corinth also wanted to row. Not only that, a further twenty-eight relatives wanted to come as passengers. And Peleus said he would come to see us settled in our new home. With Medea and me, that made seventy-three altogether on board. Then Argus said he would have to come to make sure we docked *Argo* properly. I nearly said we should limit the number to, say, sixty, but then I thought, "What the hell?" and agreed to everything. Seventy-four it was, plus luggage. I thought Argus would have objected to the loading, but he seemed to have every confidence that the load would not lower *Argo* in the water with the sea-level covering the top line on its side.

He was right. I was last on board as captain and I checked the water level. It was lapping the top line. A small crowd from the town came to see us off. I looked down from the prow as we cast off to wave to them, and there among them was the same old hag I had seen on previous occasions. She grinned, showing horrible decayed teeth, and cried, "Thank you Jason and good luck!"

I enjoyed the journey down the coast. We were in no hurry and had three overnight stops at ports where we were entertained almost royally. News of our successful adventure had spread throughout Greece like wildfire, and already the stories varied from nearly accurate to apocryphal.

And so we arrived at Corinth. The king of Corinth, Creon, laid on an extravagant feast for us, after which all my friends and their relatives dispersed by land and sea for their homes.

I was treated by the Corinthians as a famous hero who had led the greatest expedition the world had ever witnessed. It didn't last long. Medea and I settled down to domesticity in a pleasant house near the palace. Creon gave us invitations to dinner from time to time, though these gradually became more and more infrequent. During the passing years I made several trips to visit Peleus at Cheiron's school and later at Phthia, and there was a grand reunion of nearly everybody called 'The Great Calydonian Boar-hunt' at which Peleus proved to be more than a little accident-prone; but that is another story.

After ten years had passed by, a great tragedy occurred in my life, the details of which I find too painful to relate. I will give you the bare bones of what happened:

Life with Medea became unbearable. I married Creon's daughter. Medea sent our two sons with the gift of a robe to my bride. It was poisoned and when she put it on it killed her and Creon who, embracing his dying daughter, died with her. She also killed our two sons on their return and escaped to Athens with their corpses on her dragon-drawn chariot. Aegeus king of Athens sheltered her: she had promised to cure him of his childlessness.

There, that is what happened. I was left with nothing of value. Perhaps I deserved it.

I spent my remaining years wandering from city to city, living off my past fame as the captain of the *Argo*, but towards the end I returned to Corinth. I lived in a little hut near the sea, away from the city, overlooking *Argo*'s resting place. She was rotting gently. During the night I sometimes slept under the quarterdeck while during the day I lay on the beach, sheltered from the sun by her prow while I looked up at the sky and recalled all the wonderful companionship of my Argonaut friends.

Then one day, I was spending my siesta under her prow, gazing at the scudding clouds, when I suddenly saw the figure-head of Athena, carved from the Dodonian oak, falling off the prow and descending rapidly towards my head, crying as it came:

**COME
IN
NUMBER
ONE
YOUR
TIME
IS
UP!**

61

Epilogue

Here in the Elysian Fields, time passes in an indescribable way.

Distances too are irrelevant.

For example I can at this moment (or any other moment for that matter) see Medea and Achilles having a discussion about something sometime somewhere. Perhaps it is easier for you earthlings to understand if I translate that statement into something like:

"I can see Medea and Achilles having a discussion now

over on the far side of the field from where I am standing."

Incidentally, perhaps I forgot to tell you that they got married. Well, they deserved each other. Ideally suited. Very happy too, from what I hear.

It's all very pleasant here. It makes a change from my years after moving to Corinth. I can reminisce as much as I like about my school days and my exciting adventure fetching the Golden Fleece (though there were some unpleasant moments on that trip too).

I must close this chapter soon. Peleus has just popped over for a natter. Very pleasant too, but he will keep reminding me that numeracy is irrelevant here. There is certainly nothing to apply it to. Perhaps I should invent a numeracy which is not applied to anything. A kind of pure numeracy. I must work on it. I understand you already have. Aren't you lucky?

Cheiron has just trotted up.

"What are you two up to, then?" he asks, laughing from his waist up. "Tell you what: why don't you two jump up on my back and we go for a gentle canter round these fields?"

I pretend to be surprised. I reply, "You'd have lost your cool if we had suggested such a thing back on the slopes of Mount Pelion."

Cheiron says, "But it's all very different now, isn't it?"

Peleus and I jump on his back and off we trot.

FANTASTIC!

Glossary

List of the Argonauts

I believe this list agrees with the names as recorded by Apollonius of Rhodes in his epic Greek poem *Argonautica*.

Acastus, son of King Pelias of Iolcos. Pelias arranged the expedition mainly because he thought it would get rid of me. Little did he realise that so many heroes, human and divine, would volunteer to join it, particularly his own son. But Acastus insisted on coming, against his father's wishes. Good for him!

Admetus, son of Pheres, King of Pherae. Admetus later succeeded to his father's throne while his father was still young, and his future was quite eventful, but that is another story.

Aethalides, kinsman of Erytus and Echion, was the son of Hermes and Eupolemeia, daughter of Myrmidon who was the ancestor of the Myrmidons, a Thessalian people who were later ruled by Achilles. Aethalides was the expedition's herald, but was not often needed in this capacity.

Amphidamas, son of Aleus, brother of **Cepheus**. These brothers came from Tegea in Arcadia, and were the sons of Aleus. They had an elder brother named Lycurgus, but he remained at home to look after their father. However, to please his two younger brothers, Lycurgus let his son, Ancaeus, go with them.

Amphion, brother of **Asterius**.
These brothers were the sons of Hyperasius, and came from Pellene, a town in Achaia in the north of the Peloponnese which was founded by their grandfather Pelles. Useful all-rounders.

Ancaeus (1), eldest son of Lycurgus, and nephew of Amphidamas and Cepheus. His grandfather, Aleus, did not want his grandson to risk himself on the expedition, so he hid all his gear in the deepest corner of their barn. So Ancaeus came dressed in a bearskin from a bear he caught on Mount Maenalus and brandishing a huge two-edged axe in his right hand. Because of his great strength, I assigned him to row on the same bench opposite Heracles.

Ancaeus (2) of Parthenia, later called Samos, an island off the coast of Asia Minor, to the north-west of Miletus. Brother of **Erginus**.
These two were sons of Poseidon. They were both excellent seamen and warriors. After the death of Tiphys, it was this Ancaeus who took over as steersman of the *Argo*. Strangely enough he and Ancaeus (1) shared the same name and the same fate: both were killed after the expedition, quite separately, by boars.

Areius, brother of **Talaus** and **Leodocus**. These three came from Argos in the Peloponnese, and were the sons of Bias and Pero, the beautiful daughter of Neleus, twin brother of Pelias and king of Pylos in the western Peloponnese. Bias was my cousin, a son of my uncle Amythaon, my father Aeson's brother.

Quite a close-knit family, I think.

Argus, the master shipwright. Nobody thought he would want to sail in his own ship, but he did. He said that the *Argo* was the best thing he had ever built so far, and he did not want a lot of jumped-up aristocrats fooling around in it. I told him he would have to take his turn at the oars like the rest, to which he replied that if they followed his method of operating an oar, the ship had some slight chance of getting out of harbour without damage.

"In any case," he asked me, "have you any idea how to mend a boat when you damage it, as inevitably you will if left to your own devices?" Of course he had to come.

Asterion. He came from Peiresiae, a town on the plain of Thessaly, situated near the point where the rivers Apidanos and Enipeus meet to flow into the great river Peneus which flows out of Thessaly into the Aegean through the tremendous gorge of Tempe which separates mount Olympus to its north and Mount Ossa in northern Magnesia to its south. I understand that he was chosen as a champion rower, with years of practice on the many rivers round his home town.

Asterius, brother of **Amphion**. These brothers were the sons of Hyperasius, and came from Pellene, a town in Achaia in the north of the Peloponnese which was founded by their grandfather Pelles. Useful all-rounders.

Augeias, the wealthy king of Elis in the Peloponnese. His father was alleged to be Helios, the Sun-god, though I suspect this could have been a figment of Augeias's imagination. His mother was Hyrmine, a daughter of Neleus. He told me he was keen to take part in the expedition because he wanted to meet his half-brother king Aeetes (who also was a son of Helios) at Colchis. A strange man. Some time after the expedition he neglected mucking out his stables (he had inherited pedigree herds from his father) to such an extent that they were polluting the lands around them. Heracles, as his fifth labour for Eurystheus, had to clean them up. But that really is another story.

Butes (or **Boutes**), son of Teleon, from Attica (the land of the Kekrops, its first legendary king). His descendants, the Butidae, later became famous at Athens.

Calais, brother of **Zetes**. These were the twin sons of Boreas, the North Wind. Boreas once swept Oreithyia, daughter of Erechtheus, king of Athens, off her feet while she was dancing on the banks of the River Ilissus, and carried her off to his home in Thrace, way up to the north of the Aegean sea, to the rock of Sarpedon near the River Erginus. He wrapped her in murky clouds and had his way with her. She bore him the twins, Zetes and Calais, who inherited their father's ability to fly. They had dark wings sparkling with golden scales fluttering from their temples and their feet, When they flew, their long hair streamed in the wind over their shoulders and down their backs, a sight which always filled me with wonder.

Canthus of Euboea. Good man but unfortunately he was destined not to return home.

Castor of Sparta (twin brother of **Polydeuces**), master of horse racing. These twins were the sons of Leda and either her husband Tyndareus (a Lacedaemonian or Spartan hero) or Zeus himself (masquerading as a swan), both of whom slept with Leda during the same night. They were borne by Leda at the same time as another pair of twins, Helen and Clytemnestra, both of whom caused a lot of trouble later on. Their curious and somewhat ambiguous parentage gave me the opportunity to ask Castor and Polydeuces questions like "How's your dad?" which invariably elicited a ribald response. The skill of Polydeuces as a boxer came in useful on the expedition, but Castor's skill with horses was not much use, though he was a brave warrior.

Cepheus, son of Aleus, brother of **Amphidamas**. These brothers came from Tegea in Arcadia, and were the sons of Aleus. They had an elder brother named Lycurgus, but he remained at home to look after their father. However, to please his two younger brothers, Lycurgus let his son, Ancaeus, go with them.

Clytius, son of Eurytus, brother of **Iphitus (1)**. Clytius and Iphitus were guardians of Oechalia in Euboea. Eurytus, their father, was an archer who was renowned for his skill with the bow. According to Homer, he made the mistake of challenging Apollo who slew him for his presumption. His great bow was inherited by Iphitus who later gave it to Odysseus, who used it to slay the suitors of his wife Penelope. But that certainly is another story.

Coronus of Gyrton, six miles north of Larissa on the east plain of Thessaly. He was son of Caeneus the unconquerable, and described as brave, but not braver than his father. Caeneus was originally a girl, Caenis, daughter of the Lapith chieftain Elatus. She was raped by Poseidon but later changed by him into an invulnerable man at her request. As Caeneus, he married and had a son, Coronus. Later, he took part in the battle against the centaurs but they could not kill him. Finally they beat him with fir trees and buried him alive, but he survived as a flamingo. This was a difficult act for Coronus to follow.

Echion, twin brother of **Erytus**. Echion and Erytus came from Alope, on the coast of Locris, and were sons of the god Hermes by Antianeira, the daughter of Menetes, and were endowed with all of Hermes's guile. They thought up cunning plans and informed me of them.

Erginus of Miletus, a city across the Aegean sea, on the coast of Asia Minor (Turkey). Brother of **Ancaeus (2)**. These two were sons of Poseidon. Both were excellent seamen and warriors. After the death of Tiphys, it was this

Ancaeus who took over as steersman of the *Argo*. Strangely enough he and Ancaeus (1) shared the same name and the same fate: both were killed after the expedition, quite separately, by boars.

Eribotes, son of Teleon, about whom I remember very little.

Erytus, twin brother of **Echion**. Erytus and Echion came from Alope, on the coast of Locris, and were sons of the god Hermes by Antianeira, the daughter of Menetes, and were endowed with all of Hermes's guile. They thought up cunning plans and informed me of them.

Euphemus of Taenarum, the southernmost point of the Peloponnese, on the middle of its three southern promontories. His parents were Poseidon and Europa, daughter of Tityus. His father gave him the ability to walk on water, and he could run so swiftly over water that he did not get his feet wet. I was amazed to see that only tips of his toes sank in the water. He was very useful on the expedition particularly when we needed to moor the *Argo* at difficult shores.

Eurydamas, son of Ctimenus. He came from Ctimene, a town at the south of the west plain of Thessaly, not far from Lake Xynias. A useful Argonaut but I cannot remember much about him.

Eurytion, son of Irus who was a son of Actor. Peleus told me that he had fallen out of favour with him temporarily, but I think what really happened was that married life with Eurytion's daughter Antigone did not suit him. Whatever the reason for Peleus leaving Phthia and coming to see Cheiron's school, it did not stop Eurytion wanting to join the expedition and he and Peleus got on fine together.

Heracles, born in Thebes, son of Zeus (no less) and Alcmene, wife of Amphitryon. He was in the middle of one of his labours for Erystheus when he heard about our expedition. He had just left the region of Arcadia in the Peloponnese at the time and was carrying on his back a live boar which had been feeding in the thickets of mount Lampeia near the Erymanthian swamp. He dropped it immediately, tied it up, left it at the entrance to the market at Mycenae and hot-footed it to join us. What a man!

Hylas, the son of Theiodamas, king of the Dryopes. Heracles carried him off from his father whom he killed after a quarrel. Hylas became his noble squire and lover and accompanied him, carrying his bow and arrows.

Idas, the boaster, son of Aphareus, brother of **Lyncaeus**. These brothers came from Arene, on the west coast of Messenia in the Peloponnese. They were both very strong and knew it. Idas was lacking in modesty, to put it mildly. Lyncaeus had the sharpest eye-sight I have ever experienced, and it seemed as though he could actually see through things.

Idmon, from Argos. He was a son of Apollo, though his mortal father was Abas, the son of Melampus, son of my uncle Amythaon. His divine parentage endowed him with the art of prophesy, through the observation of the behaviour of birds and the signs in burnt-offerings. He predicted a successful outcome of the expedition, though he himself was fated to die before its conclusion.

Iphiclus (1) [there were two men named *Iphiclus* on the expedition: see Iphiclus (2) below] Jason's maternal uncle of Phylace, another town of Thessaly, situated in the mountainous regions about twelve miles (as the crow flies) south-west of Pherae. He was a brother of Alcimede who was Jason's mother. He was chosen, not only because of his kinship to Jason, but because of his speed at running. It was said that he could race against the winds; he could run over a field of corn and not crush it and skim over the ears of wheat and not damage the crop. I never saw him do this.

Iphiclus (2), son of Thestius and brother of Althaea who was mother of Meleager. He was a good fighter, both with the javelin and hand-to-hand.

Iphitus (1), son of Eurytus, brother of **Clytius**. Iphitus and Clytius were guardians of Oechalia in Euboea. Eurytus, their father, was an archer who was renowned for his skill with the bow. According to Homer, he made the mistake of challenging Apollo who slew him for his presumption. His great bow was inherited by Iphitus who later gave it to Odysseus, who used it to slay the suitors of his wife Penelope. But that is another story.

Iphitus (2), king of Phocis. He was son of Naubolus, son of Ornytus. He put me up in his palace and entertained me royally when I went to consult the Oracle at Delphi concerning the expedition. Of course he had to come on the expedition.

Jason, son of Aeson, rightful heir to throne of Iolcos. I nearly forgot to list myself.

Laocoon, son of Porthaon and a slave-woman. Brother of Oeneus, king of Calydon. Although perhaps past his prime as a warrior, he was sent on the expedition by Oeneus to look after his son, Meleager, who also had his uncle Iphiclus (2) to keep an eye on him.

Leodocus, brother of **Talaus** and **Areius**. These three came from Argos in the Peloponnese, and were the sons of Bias and Pero, the beautiful daughter of Neleus, twin brother of Pelias and king of Pylos in the western Peloponnese. Bias was my cousin, a son of my uncle Amythaon, my father Aeson's brother.

Quite a close-knit family. I think.

Lyncaeus the sharp-eyed, son of Aphareus, brother of **Idas**. These brothers came from Arene, on the west coast of Messenia in the Peloponnese. They were both very strong and knew it. Idas was lacking in modesty, to put it mildly. Lyncaeus had the sharpest eye-sight I have ever experienced, and it seemed as though he could actually see through things.

Meleager of Calydon, a town in Aetolia (southern mainland Greece, opposite the northern Peloponnese), to the west of Naupactos. Son of Oeneus and Althaea, a sister of Leda. He was a very brave fighter, though very young; another year or two and he would have one of the best.

Menoetius, son of Actor and Aegina. He came from Opus on the coast of Locris. He later became father of Patroclus who fought at Troy.

Mopsus, from Thessaly. He fought in the battle between to Lapiths and the centaurs. He could understand the language of birds, having been taught their language by Apollo himself, and was a soothsayer on the expedition, second in importance to Idmon.

Nauplius, son of Clytoneus, and ultimately descended from king Danaus, but I shall spare you the full details. His great-great-great-grandfather was also called Nauplius, who was himself an expert seaman.

Oileus, a warrior of outstanding courage. In battle he was the first to follow hard after a fleeing foe.

Orpheus, the great musician. Borne by Calliope, one of the Muses, to her Thracian lover, Oeagrus. Men say that the sound of his songs could enchant the solid rocks and the gushing torrents of mountains. As evidence, on the coast of Thrace, there can be seen row upon row of wild oak trees growing in thick profusion, which he charmed with his lyre all the way down from the mountains. He was very useful on the expedition by calming the waves and heartening the crew.

Palaemonius, from Olenus in Aitolia. He was the son of Hephaestus, which may have accounted for the fact that he was crippled in both feet. However he overcame this disability by maintaining a high level of overall and bravery, agility and strength which in many ways made him superior to most other Argonauts.

Peleus, son of Aeacus, officially from Phthia. Responsible with others for drawing up the list of potential Argonauts. With typical modesty, he invited himself. His main functions on the expedition (according to him) was keeping an eye on me and fulfilling the role of accident prevention officer, with particular attention to matters of health and safety.

Periclymenus, the oldest son of Neleus of Pylos. His grandfather Poseidon endowed him with boundless strength and the ability to change himself into any form he might want. This ability extricated him from many a tight corner in battle.

Phalerus, nicknamed "Ashspear". He was the only son of Alcon, who let him come, even though he had no-one else to look after him in his old age. Very noble of him.

Phlias, from a town in the north-east Peloponnese named Phlius after him, on the River Asopus which flows northward into the Corinthian Gulf. He was a son of Dionysus, no less, and Araithyrea, daughter of Minyas.

Polydeuces (known later as Pollux) of Sparta (twin brother of **Castor**), champion boxer. These twins were the sons of Leda and either her husband Tyndareus (a Lacedaemonian or Spartan hero) or Zeus himself (masquerading as a swan), both of whom slept with Leda during the same night. They were borne by Leda at the same time as another pair of twins, Helen and Clytemnestra, both of whom caused a lot of trouble later on. Their curious parentage gave me the opportunity to ask Castor and Polydeuces questions like "How's your dad?" which invariably elicited a ribald response. The skill of Polydeuces as a boxer came in useful on the expedition, but Castor's skill with horses was not much use, though he was a brave warrior.

Polyphemus, from Larissa, a major city in the east plain of Thessaly, on the right bank of the River Peneus, and about twenty-five miles north-west of Pherae across the plain. In his youth he had fought with the mighty Lapiths (a Thessalian clan) in their war against the centaurs; he was no longer young but was still a warrior to be respected.

Talaus, brother of **Areius** and **Leodocus**. These three came from Argos in the Peloponnese, and were the sons of Bias and Pero, the beautiful daughter of Neleus, twin brother of Pelias and king of Pylos in the western Peloponnese. Bias was my cousin, a son of my uncle Amythaon, my father Aeson's brother.

Quite a close-knit family. I think.

Telamon, son of Aeacus, from Salamis. Peleus had to invite his own brother, who was unlikely to let Peleus get all the glory.

Tiphys, son of Hagnias, from Siphae, a town on the southern coast of Boeotia. He was an expert mariner who was able to sense a coming swell across the sea, could feel the onset of storms and could use the sun or stars to navigate. I chose him to be helmsman at the start of the expedition.

Zetes, brother of **Calais**.
These were the twin sons of Boreas, the North Wind. Boreas once swept Oreithyia, daughter of Erechtheus, king of Athens, off her feet while she was dancing on the banks of the River Ilissus, and carried her off to his home in Thrace, way up to the north of the Aegean sea, to the rock of Sarpedon near the River Erginus. He wrapped her in murky clouds and had his way with her. She bore him the twins, Zetes and Calais, who inherited their father's ability to fly. They had dark wings sparkling with golden scales fluttering from their temples and their feet. When they flew, their long hair streamed in the wind over their shoulders and down their backs, a sight which always filled me with wonder.

That makes fifty-five altogether, including me. I know Argus said we needed only fifty-four, but with Peleus in charge of the roll-call, are you really surprised? He said that he forgot to include himself in the count. Typical!

ARGO'S JOURNEY FROM
IOLCOS TO COLCHIS

Map One

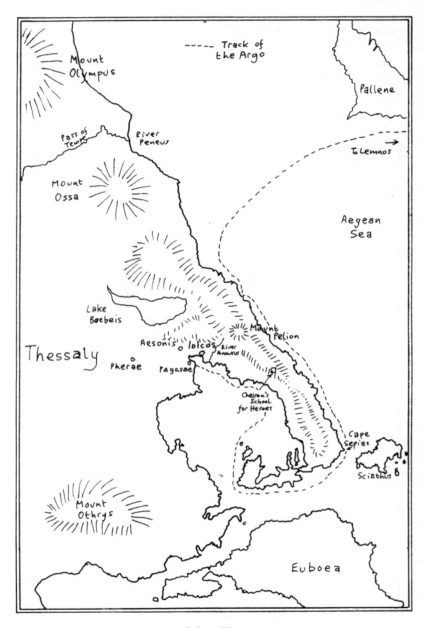

Map Two

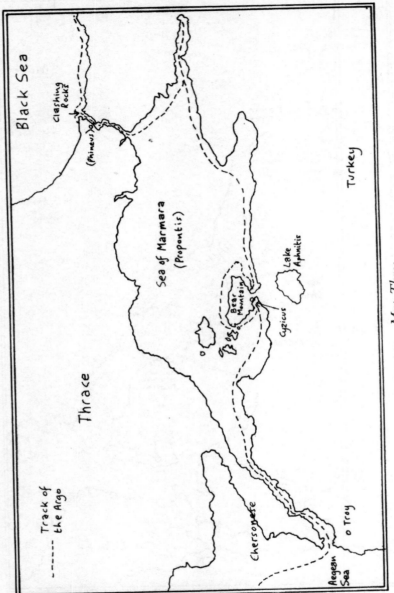

Map Three

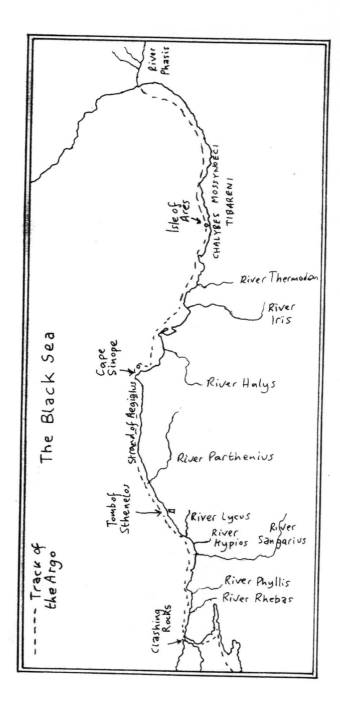

Map Four

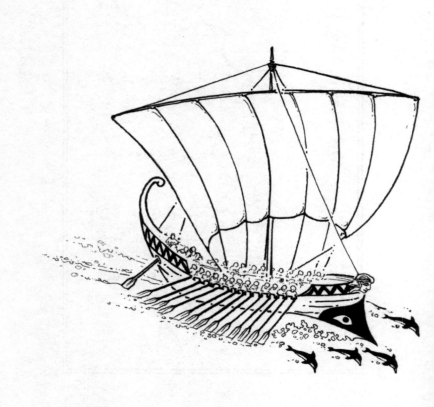